GRADE **4** Student Workbook

BIBLE CURRICULUM

Walking With God and His People

THIRD
EDITION

JOY BEGGS

CHRISTIAN SCHOOLS INTERNATIONAL

GRAND RAPIDS, MICHIGAN

credo
house publishers

Credo House Publishers, Grand Rapids, MI 49525
www.credocommunications.net

Printed in the United States of America

18 17 16 15 14 13 12 11 10 09   2 3 4 5 6 7 8 9 10

ISBN: 978-1-935391-11-1

The development of *Walking With God and His People* was made possible
with grants from Christian Schools International Foundation,
Canadian Christian Education Foundation, Inc., and
Richard & Helen DeVos Foundation.

General Editor: Timothy Beals
Managing Editor: Donna Huisjen
Copyeditor: Elizabeth Banks
Illustrator: Steven Thomason
Cover design: Sharon VanLoozenoord
Interior design and composition: Sharon VanLoozenoord
Bible Dictionary photographs: John and Melanie DeKruyter

Christian Schools International
3350 East Paris Ave SE
Grand Rapids, Michigan 49512-3054

The Five Ws of the Book of Philippians

Name _Sonia Lau_
_9/8/17_

1. Read Philippians 1:1 and answer the following questions.

    a. Who wrote the Book of Philippians? _The apostle Paul wrote Phillippians._

    b. To whom was the book written? _It was written to the church at Philippi._

2. What could be the theme verse of Philippians? Write it out. _The theme verse is Philippians 4:4-5 "Rejoice in the Lord always, I will say it again: Rejoice!"_

3. When was the letter to the Philippians written? <u>Although there is not a verse in the Book of Philippians that tells when this letter was written, we can deduce the answer from some passages in the Book of Philippians and elsewhere in Scripture, as well as from history. The Book of Philippians was written somewhere between A.D. 60 and 63, most likely in early A.D. 63.</u>

4. Where was Philippians written from? Philippians 1:7, 13, 14, 17 _In prison._

5. Why was the book written? Match the reference with Paul's reason for writing.

a. Philippians 2:25; 4:10–18

b. Philippians 2:25–30

c. Philippians 1:12–20

d. Philippians 1:25–26; 2:19–24

e. Philippians 3:2–3, 18–19

f. Philippians 1:27–30; 4:1

g. Philippians 4:2–3

To inform them of his well-being and future plans.

To encourage them to stand firm.

To let them know that Epaphroditus was fine and was returning to them.

To exhort two women to "agree in the Lord."

To thank them for their gifts.

To warn them of false teachers.

To inform them about the spread of the gospel.

The Church at Philippi

Name Sonia Lau
Sept. 8, 2017

Summarize what we learn about the recipients of Paul's letter from the following verses in Philippians.

1. How does Paul describe them?

   a. 1:5 _partnership in the gospel._

   b. 1:12 _brothers and sisters._

   c. 2:12 _dear friends._

   d. 4:1 _brothers and sisters, dear friends, joy and crown._

2. What did they do?

   a. 1:19 _they prayed._

   b. 4:9 _they learned and received from Paul._

   c. 4:15–16 _sent Paul aids._

3. What were their circumstances?

   a. 1:28; 3:1–2 _they had opponents._

   b. 1:29 _suffering._

   c. 1:30 _struggleing with Paul._

4. What was Paul's relationship to them?

   a. 1:3 _he was thankful for them._

   b. 1:8 _longs for them._

   c. 1:9 _he loves them._

   d. 2:2, 19 _They bring joy to him._

   e. 4:1 _he loved them and longed for them._

5. I can be more like the Philippians by _being kind_.

Paul's Message to the Philippians

Name _9/11/17_

The Philippians knew that Paul's message was genuine. It came from Paul's experience and from his love for them. Read the following passages and finish the sentences to summarize the message Paul wanted to convey.

1. **1:12–18**   Paul's problems served to _advance the gospel._

2. **1:20–26**   Paul's desire was to _have sufficient courage so that now as always Christ will be exalted in his body, whether by life or death._

3. **2:1–4**   Paul stressed the importance of _being like minded._

4. **2:5–11**   Christians need to follow Jesus' example of _becoming obedient to death being humble_

5. **2:12–15**   The way God's people live should _be blameless and pure. ~~Do ev~~ an example to the world._

6. **3:2–4**   Beware of _those dogs, those evildoers, those mutilators of flesh._

7. **3:7–11**   More important than anything else is _that Christ is our Lord._

8. **3:12–14**   Paul didn't "have it all together" but was _pressing on to take hold of that for which Jesus took hold of him._

9. **4:4–9**   Be characterized by _rejoicing in the Lord always._

10. **4:10–13**   In any situation, Paul had learned to _be content no matter what happened._

11. **4:14–19**   The Philippians were praised for _praising the Lord. for giving_

Followers of Christ

Name _____

In addition to the apostle Paul, other followers of Christ can be studied from the Book of Philippians. Read each passage and fill in the blanks to tell how each person was following Christ's example.

1. **Timothy (2:19–24)**   He took a _genuine concern_ in their welfare. He _longs_ himself through his actions, serving with Paul.

2. **Epaphroditus (2:25–30)**   He was a brother, fellow _co-worker_, and fellow _soldier_ whom the Philippians sent to _take care of my needs_.

3. **Euodia and Syntyche (4:2–3)**   They contended at Paul's side in the _cause of the gospel_.

4. **Clement (4:3)**   He was a fellow _co-worker_.

5. We can learn from the Book of Philippians how following Christ involved various people with different gifts. Think of how you can serve Christ with the gifts that God has given you. Draw a picture below showing one way in which you can be a follower of Christ.

Be Joyful!

The word *joy* or synonyms for joy are found 16 times in the Book of Philippians. Below are some of them. Read the following verses and their context, and fill in the blanks.

1. "In all my prayers for all of you, I always _pray with joy_____" (1:4).

2. "Christ is _preached_____. And because of this I <u>rejoice</u>" (1:18).

3. "I will continue with all of you for your progress and _joy in the faith_____" (1:25).

4. "Through my being with you again your joy in Christ Jesus will _overflow_____ on account of me" (1:26).

5. "Make my <u>joy</u> complete by being _like-minded_____" (2:2).

6. "But even if I am being poured out like a _drink offering_____ . . . I am glad and <u>rejoice</u> with all of you" (2:17).

7. "So you too should be _glad and rejoice_____ with me" (2:18).

8. "When you see him again you may be <u>glad</u> and I may have less _anxiety_____" (2:28).

9. "_Welcome_____ him in the Lord with great joy, and honor men like him" (2:29).

10. "Finally, _brothers and sisters_, rejoice in the Lord!" (3:1).

11. "Therefore, my brothers . . . my _joy and my crown_____, that is how you should stand firm in the Lord, dear friends!" (4:1).

12. "Rejoice in the Lord _always_____. I will say it again: Rejoice!" (4:4).

From the Book of Philippians we can learn:

1. Real joy comes from knowing _Christ_____.

2. We can be joyful in every _situation_____.

3. Joy is maintained through _prayer_____, _fellowship_____, and _thanksgiving_____.

Masaki's Umbrella

Narrator: Our story takes place on a little island. Masaki lived in a village there. It was a special event in his life to be able to take a boat trip to the big island and visit the shops in the capital city. One day he boarded the boat to take the long journey to the big island. He had been saving his money for a long time and was planning to buy something special. Two of his friends gathered at the boat as Masaki climbed aboard.

Friend 1: Have a good time, Masaki.

Friend 2: We'll be waiting to see what you buy.

Masaki: So long. I'll see you later.

Narrator: When Masaki got to the big island, he went to a shop in the city, checking now and then to be sure that his money was still in his pocket. He looked over the many things in the store. Suddenly he picked up an umbrella.

Masaki: What is this, sir?

Storekeeper: That is a very important thing to have on these islands, Masaki. It is an umbrella. It will keep you dry in the rain.

Masaki (with wide eyes): Wow! I'll take one. My friends will really think I'm smart when I go out in the rain and don't even get wet!

Narrator: Masaki paid the storekeeper and left the store with the umbrella on his arm and a smile on his face. He got back on the boat and headed for home. After a while he could see his friends waiting along the shore.

Friends: Hello! Welcome back!

Friend 1: What's that, Masaki? Did you get it in the city?

(Friends gather around him and look closely at the closed umbrella.)

Masaki: Let me tell you, it's a great thing! It's called an umbrella.

(With puzzled expressions the friends look at each other, then back at the umbrella.)

Masaki: When it rains, this umbrella will keep me dry!

Friend 1: That's amazing!

Friend 2: Hey, we'll be around when it rains, Masaki. We want to see this umbrella work!

Narrator: It wasn't long before Masaki had a chance to try out his new umbrella.

(Show a sign that says, "Rain is falling.")

Narrator: Masaki's friends ran to the door of his house and called to him to come out. Masaki came to the door and looked out. He went back in and then came out with his umbrella. He walked out very smartly with the umbrella swinging on his arm.

(Laughing as Masaki gets soaked with rain.)

Friend 1: Masaki, you really got a bargain there!

Masaki: There's something wrong. The storekeeper said I wouldn't get wet. He must have sold me a bad umbrella. I'll take it back and get another one.

Narrator: Masaki went back to the big island.

Masaki (to storekeeper): What's the matter with this umbrella? I took it out with me in the rain and I got soaked!

Storekeeper: Did you hold it over your head?

Masaki: No. I didn't know I was supposed to do that!

Storekeeper: You take this umbrella back home. And the next time the rain comes, hold it over your head, and it will work perfectly.

Narrator: Masaki smiled, thanked the storekeeper, and ran for the boat with the umbrella swinging on his arm. His friends were waiting for him when he got back.

Masaki: I know the problem now. Just you wait until it rains again; I'll show you something great. I won't get wet—not one bit!

Narrator: When it rained that afternoon, Masaki held the closed umbrella over his head. His friends laughed, and he got soaked. So he went back to the city.

Masaki: I want my money back! This umbrella is no good. I got soaked again!

Storekeeper: I can't understand it, Masaki. It's a good umbrella. You opened it up and held it just like this? *(He demonstrates.)*

Masaki: I have to open it up?

Storekeeper: Yes, Masaki, that's the way you keep dry. You open the umbrella, hold it over your head like this, and the rain rolls off around you.

Masaki: Wait until my friends see this!

Narrator: When it rained later that day, Masaki opened the umbrella, held it over his head, and stayed dry.

Friends: Hooray!

Narrator: Maybe you are thinking, "Masaki was silly not to open that umbrella!" This story reminds me of something that all of you have—a Bible. You need to do more than carry your umbrella to keep from getting wet. You also need to do more than own a Bible to learn to please God. God's Word will help you, but only if you open it and use it!

Pictographs

Draw pictographs for the following messages.

1. The dog ate my homework.

2. I'm going to the beach with my friends.

3. I live at the corner of Maple Street and Third Avenue.

Draw a pictograph, and then have a partner guess the message.

Hieroglyphics: Egyptian Picture Writing

Rules for Hieroglyphics

1. A hieroglyphic can be a picture of a word.

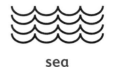

sea

eye

2. A hieroglyphic can be a picture that sounds the same as a word.

see

I

3. A hieroglyphic can be a picture symbol of an idea.

life

ruler

4. A hieroglyphic can stand for a sound or a combination of sounds.

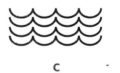

c

i

On the other side of this sheet, write a favorite Bible story in hieroglyphics.

Write the name of your Bible story here. _____

The Development of Writing

	Canaanite 1500 B.C.	Hebrew 700 B.C.	Hebrew 1st century B.C.	Greek	Latin
ox				A	A
house				B	B
throw-stick				F	G
fish				△	D
man with raised arms				E	E
prop				Y	FY
weapon?				Z	Z
fence?				H	H
				I	I
palm of hand				K	K
staff				L	L
water				M	M
snake				N	N
eye				O	O
mouth				Γ	P
monkey?					Q
head				P	R
bow?				Ϟ	S
cross mark				T	T

Write a favorite Bible verse using the symbols from one of the languages. If a letter does not have a symbol, design one of your own, or use the letter from the English alphabet.

_____

_____

_____

_____

_____

_____

_____

The Writing of the Bible

Each of the following examples is a well-known Bible passage written in the Hebrew style. Use your knowledge of how Hebrew was written to "translate" the passage to English.

1. TNWNBTNLLHSDRHPHSYMSDRLHT

   _____

   _____

2. NSYLNDNNSHVGHTHTDLRWHTDVLSDGRF

   _____

   _____

3. DRPTNSTTSBTNSDTYVNTNSDTDNKSVLTNTPSVL

   _____

   _____

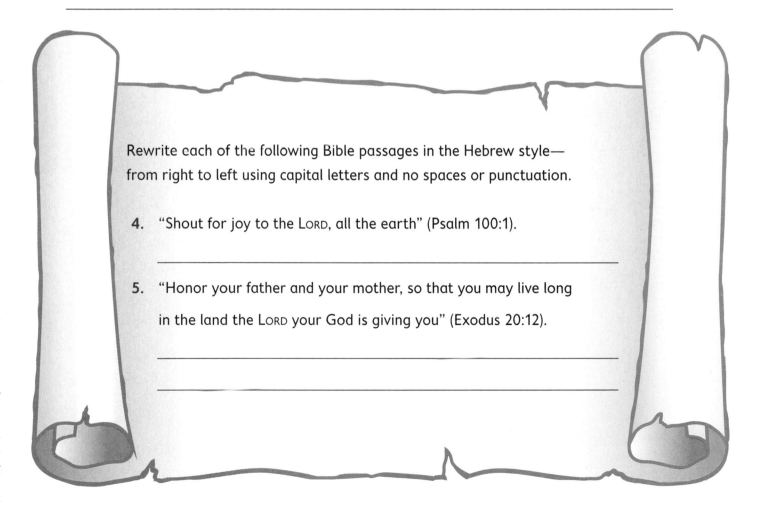

Rewrite each of the following Bible passages in the Hebrew style— from right to left using capital letters and no spaces or punctuation.

4. "Shout for joy to the LORD, all the earth" (Psalm 100:1).

   _____

5. "Honor your father and your mother, so that you may live long in the land the LORD your God is giving you" (Exodus 20:12).

   _____

   _____

Divisions of the Old Testament

Name _____

Your teacher will read information about the four types of books in the Old Testament. As you listen to the information, write down the main descriptions of each division.

Pentateuch

_____

_____

_____

_____

Pentateuch books: _____

_____

Historical Books

_____

_____

_____

_____

_____

Historical books: _____

_____

Books of Poetry

_____

_____

_____

_____

_____

Poetry books: _____

Genesis
Exodus
Leviticus
Numbers
Deuteronomy
Joshua
Judges
Ruth
1 Samuel
2 Samuel
1 Kings
2 Kings
1 Chronicles
2 Chronicles
Ezra
Nehemiah
Esther
Job
Psalms
Proverbs
Ecclesiastes
Song of Songs

Books of Prophecy

_____

_____

_____

_____

Prophecy books: _____

_____

_____

Storing the Bible

The Israelites kept the scrolls of the Old Testament in storage jars. Cut out the scrolls from the next page. Paste them on the proper jars, with the names of the books in the correct order.

Scrolls

CUT

Genesis	Amos	2 Kings
Job	Numbers	Song of Songs
Esther	Ecclesiastes	Joshua
Jonah	Malachi	Isaiah
Exodus	Hosea	Ezekiel
Psalms	Nahum	Judges
Nehemiah	Haggai	Jeremiah
Obadiah	Habakkuk	Lamentations
Micah	Zephaniah	Ruth
Zechariah	Deuteronomy	1 Samuel
Leviticus	1 Chronicles	Daniel
Proverbs	2 Samuel	1 Kings
Ezra	Joel	2 Chronicles

CUT

The Life of Abraham

See how well you know the life of Abraham. Fill in the blanks below with words that fit inside the crossword puzzle. If you need some hints, go to Genesis chapters 12 through 25 for help. Or you may ask your teacher.

The completed crossword contains the answers:
- 1 Down: Sarai
- 2 Across: Hagar
- 2 Down: Haran
- 3 Down: ninety
- 4 Down: pharaoh
- 5 Across: sister
- 6 Across: ishmael
- 7 Down: laughter
- 8 Down: blessing
- 9 Down: Gomorrah
- 10 Down: canaan
- 11 Across: ten
- 12 Across: sacrifice
- 13 Down: faith
- 14 Down: Lot
- 15 Across: ram
- 16 Across: covenant

Across

2. Wife's maidservant, the mother of Abraham's first son.
5. Abram didn't tell the whole truth in Egypt when he said that Sarai was his _____.
6. Abram's first son.
11. God promised to not destroy Sodom if this many righteous people could be found there.
12. God told Abraham to do this to Isaac on Mount Moriah.
15. This animal was placed on the altar instead of Isaac.
16. In a vision, Abram saw carcasses of halves of animals as God made a _____ with Abram.

Down

1. Abram's first wife's original name.
2. When Abraham and Sarah were told of their coming son, God asked, "Is anything too _____ for the Lord?"
3. The age of Sarah when she gave birth to Isaac.
4. In Egypt, Sarai was taken to the _____ because of her beauty.
7. Abraham and Sarah's son was named Isaac, meaning this.
8. God promised to make Abraham's name great and to make him a _____.
9. Along with Sodom, the wicked city destroyed by God.
10. Land promised to Abraham's descendants.
13. Hebrews 11 describes people who had great _____.
14. Abraham's nephew who chose the best land.

Isaac and Jacob

Number the following statements from the account
of Isaac and Jacob in the correct order, 1–5 in each group.

4   Jacob said that he would give Esau stew in exchange for his birthright.

2   Esau become a skillful hunter, but Jacob was a quiet, at-home man.

5   Esau didn't think highly of his birthright and sold it for food.

3   Esau came home from hunting very hungry.

1   Rebekah gave birth to twins, Jacob and Esau.

3   Jacob disguised himself as Esau and brought Isaac the meal.

5   Esau planned to kill Jacob as soon as their father, Isaac, had died.

1   Isaac instructed Esau to prepare him a special meal before receiving his blessing.

4   Jacob received Isaac's blessing.

2   Rebekah suggested that Jacob trick his father and receive the blessing.

2   Jacob had a dream in which God blessed him and promised to watch over him.

4   Jacob was welcomed to stay with Laban.

5   Jacob met Rachel when she was coming to water her father's sheep.

1   Isaac blessed Jacob and sent him to Laban's household.

3   Jacob set up a pillar and called the place Bethel.

5   Laban didn't want Jacob to leave, because of the blessing he had received on account of Jacob.

1   Jacob agreed to work for Laban for seven years in exchange for his daughter Rachel.

3   Jacob had to work another seven years for Laban in order to get Rachel as his wife.

2   Laban tricked Jacob, giving him his older daughter Leah as his wife.

4   Leah bore six sons, and Rachel had two sons.

5   Esau forgave Jacob and welcomed him home.

3   Jacob wrestled with God.

2   Jacob was afraid at the thought of meeting Esau again.

1   Jacob took his family and possessions and fled from Laban.

4   Jacob offered many gifts to Esau.

Stories of Moses

Name 10/21/17

Choose one story from the life of Moses. Tell the story from a different perspective. Perhaps you are Miriam as she puts the basket in the river. Maybe you're a slave waiting for God's deliverance. You could be a child tasting manna for the first time. Use your imagination! You could even be a frog in the pharoah's palace or a fish who had a wild ride in the Red Sea! Write your story and give it a title.

My Extraordinary Throw

I was just swimming in my Red Sea as usual, you know, like I didn't even know what to do. But all of a sudden, I felt that all the waters in the sea were vibrating. At first, I only thought it was a giant shark. But really? Was it a mega giant shark? A... Ahhhhhh! I had been thrown out of the water like a huge, gigantic magnet from space or something. After that shake, the thing was giving me, I was tossed down from really, really high above. I landed with a stomach aching belly flop. Then, I noticed something only a few fish have ever seen before! There, before my own fishy little eyes, was people! Wait! Did I say that correctly? Oh, right. It was people. Like pe-op-le. Okay, way off the topic. And, I also saw reeeealy dry land. Like no fish has ever seen before! Us fishies only have heard about great myths of that before. Wasn't that amazing? I'm going to tell mom and dad fishy!

Joshua

Use the clues on the following page and the passages from the Book of Joshua to fill in the answers to the puzzle. The box will give you the theme of this lesson.

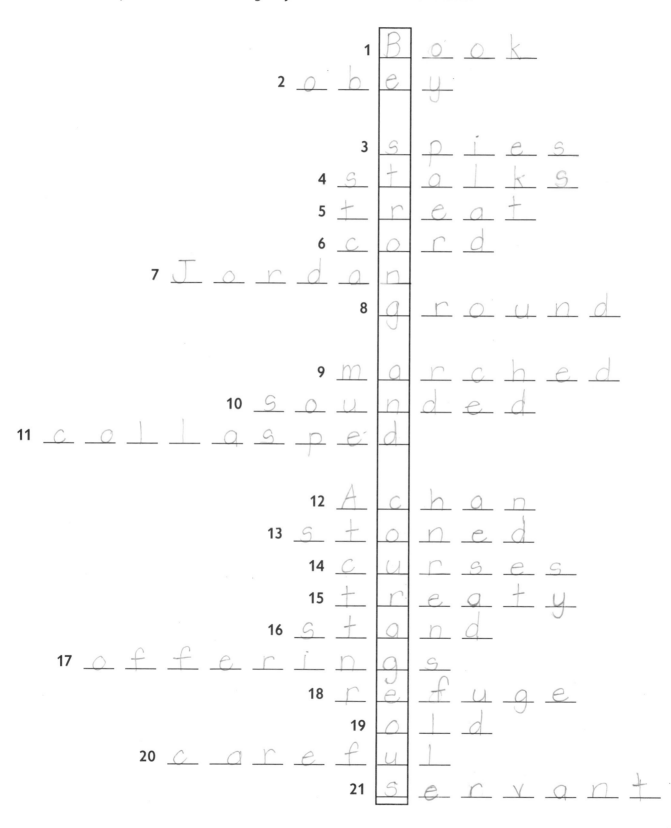

1. B o o k
2. o b e y
3. s p i e s
4. s t a l k s
5. t r e a t
6. c o r d
7. J o r d a n
8. g r o u n d
9. m a r c h e d
10. s o u n d e d
11. c o l l a s p e d
12. A c h a n
13. s t o n e d
14. c u r s e s
15. t r e a t y
16. s t a n d
17. o f f e r i n g s
18. r e f u g e
19. o l d
20. c a r e f u l
21. s e r v a n t

1. God told the new leader, Joshua, to meditate on the _Book_ of the Law. (1:8)

2. The people promised to _obey_ Joshua as they had Moses. (1:17)

3. Joshua sent two _spies_ into Jericho. (2:1)

4. Rahab hid them from the king under the _stalks_ of flax on the roof. (2:6)

5. The spies promised to _treat_ Rahab and her family kindly and faithfully. (2:14)

6. A scarlet _cord_ would be a sign of safety for Rahab and her family. (2:18–19)

7. When the priests carrying the ark of the covenant stepped into the _Jordan_ River, the water stopped flowing. (3:15–16)

8. Joshua fell facedown to the _ground_ in reverence before the commander of the Lord's army. (5:14)

9. The Israelites _marched_ around Jericho every day for six days and for seven times on the seventh day. (6:14–15)

10. The people shouted and the trumpets _sounded_. (6:20)

11. The walls of Jericho _collasped_, and the city was taken. (6:20)

12. _Achan_ hid some of the plunder from Jericho in his tent. (7:20–21)

13. The results of Achan's sin were that Ai defeated them and Achan was _stoned_. (7:25)

14. The covenant was renewed as Joshua read the blessings and the _curses_ of the law. (8:34)

15. The Gibeonites deceived Joshua into making a _treaty_ with them. (9:16)

16. In the battle against the Amorites, God made the sun _stand_ still. (10:12–13)

17. When the land was divided among the tribes, the Levites did not receive land, because the _offerings_ of the people were their inheritance. (13:14)

18. To protect people in case of accidental death, cities of _refuge_ were set up. (20:1–3)

19. When Joshua was _old_, he summoned the leaders of Israel together. (23:1–2)

20. Joshua reminded them to be _careful_ to obey all the law. (23:6)

21. Joshua, the son of Nun, the _son_ of the Lord, died at the age of 110. (24:29)

Othniel

Using Othniel's name as a base, build on it with other words or phrases that will help you remember Othniel's time as Israel's judge.

O
T
H
N
I
E
L

_____

_____

_____

_____

_____

_____

_____

Ehud

At each location on the map, write what happened in today's story.

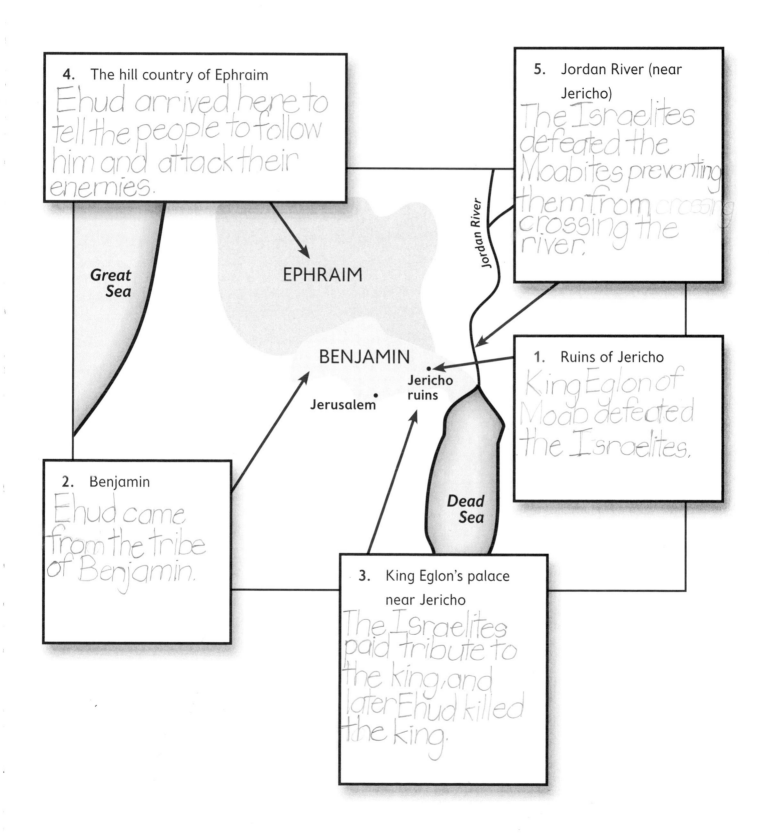

4. The hill country of Ephraim

Ehud arrived here to tell the people to follow him and attack their enemies.

5. Jordan River (near Jericho)

The Israelites defeated the Moabites preventing them from crossing crossing the river.

Great Sea

EPHRAIM

Jordan River

BENJAMIN

Jericho ruins

Jerusalem

1. Ruins of Jericho

King Eglon of Moab defeated the Israelites.

2. Benjamin

Ehud came from the tribe of Benjamin.

Dead Sea

3. King Eglon's palace near Jericho

The Israelites paid tribute to the king, and later Ehud killed the king.

Judges

Use words from the word bank to fill in the blanks in this story. You will use one of the words twice. When you are finished, find the words in the word search on the back of this page.

When Joshua and the elders lived, the Israelites served _God_. But after they all died, this began to change. The Israelites did not continue to fight against the people of Canaan, as God had commanded. Instead, they began to marry the Canaanites and worship their _gods_. God allowed the Canaanites and others to remain in the land to _test_ Israel—to see if the Israelites would obey him. When they didn't, God allowed _enemies_ to oppress Israel. When the Israelites cried to God for help, he sent _judges_ to save them.

The first judge was _Othniel_. He _fought_ against the people of Aram and defeated them. Then Israel had peace for _forty_ years.

The second judge was _Ehud_, a Benjamite. He was _left-handed_. At that time the Moabites were oppressing Israel. Israel cried out to _God_ for help, and God sent Ehud to save _Israel_. Because he was left-handed, Ehud was able to sneak a sword into the palace of Eglon, the king of _Moab_. He killed Eglon and then fled. When he returned to Israel, Ehud blew a _trumpet_ to call Israel to war. The Israelites fought the Moabites at the _Jordan_ River and killed 10,000 of them. Then Israel had peace for _eighty_ years.

Word Bank				
Ehud	**eighty**	**enemies**	**forty**	**fought**
God	**gods**	**Israel**	**Jordan**	**judges**
left-handed	**Moab**	**Othniel**	**test**	**trumpet**

O	T	H	N	I	E	L	P	R	Z	R	E	F	X	V
O	D	T	Q	Y	O	K	T	R	U	M	P	E	T	B
E	I	G	H	T	Y	J	J	F	J	I	J	O	A	D
B	Q	Q	F	B	O	F	O	U	G	H	T	O	U	V
J	O	R	D	A	N	L	G	F	X	J	M	H	D	O
O	T	T	M	M	J	U	D	G	E	S	E	E	R	D
V	N	M	L	F	Q	P	G	K	V	J	D	F	W	R
F	T	D	R	L	E	E	P	I	B	N	Q	C	F	X
E	O	E	J	J	R	D	D	S	A	Y	T	C	E	X
X	N	R	S	V	T	U	J	H	T	W	F	R	S	I
Q	V	E	T	T	W	A	T	Z	V	G	F	C	K	S
U	M	P	M	Y	G	F	B	E	C	D	G	A	V	R
J	V	W	D	I	E	O	H	Q	I	J	T	B	A	A
X	M	O	M	L	E	I	D	M	G	T	N	I	A	E
R	G	R	H	D	V	S	J	S	D	H	C	O	B	L

Word Bank

Ehud ✓	eighty ✓	enemies ✓	forty ✓	fought ✓
God ✓	gods ✓	Israel ✓	Jordan ✓	judges ✓
left-handed ✓	Moab ✓	Othniel ✓	test ✓	trumpet ✓

The Song of Deborah and Barak

Name _____ 11/28/17

Answer the following questions about the Song of Deborah and Barak from Judges 5.

1. To whom did Deborah and Barak sing? (5:3) Deborah and Barak sang to God.

2. Why did they refer to God as the One of Sinai? (5:5) They refer to God as the One of Sinai because the He spoke at the Mountain of Sinai.

3. What were the conditions like in Israel before Deborah's rule? (5:6–9) People were slaves and not praising. They did it their own ways. They joined the Canaanites.

4. Why are the words *wake up* repeated in verse 12? To emphasize that it was time for Deborah to take action and to lead the people back to God and to victory.

5. Who fought along with Deborah and Barak? Who stayed behind? (5:13–18) Ephraim, Benjamin, Zebulun, Manasseh, Issachar, and Naphtali fought. Rueben, Gad, Asher, and Dan did not fight. The other tribes hand other duties.

6. What happened to the Canaanites? (5:19–23) God fought on Israel's side, the Israelites won a great victory, and the people of Canaan were defeated.

7. What images, pictures, or exciting language are used in verses 9–23? Examples include "from the heavens the stars fought"

8. Who was the hero of the battle? How did this fulfill what Deborah had told Barak? (5:24–27)

The battle's hero was Jael. Deborah had told Barak that because he had asked her to go along the hero would be a woman.

9. To what did Deborah compare the people who loved the Lord? (5:31) She said that

Gideon and the Fleece

Even though God called Gideon, Gideon wasn't sure that he would be able to do the tasks God would give him. God also calls us to do work for him today. How can we answer God's call and do his work in the world?

Sometimes the tasks that God gives us seem difficult or even frightening, but the New Testament tells us that God will always be with us. Look up the following New Testament passages, and summarize on each package what God is promising in this verse or verses.

When God is with you, and you trust in Him, he will help you. Otherwise, he won't help you.

John 15:5

When you are with God, you are strong. When you are not with God, you are weak

2 Corinthians 12:9–10

God gives us strength

Ephesians 3:16–20

I can do anything with God helping me.

Philippians 4:13

We pray for God to give us strength

Colossians 1:9–12

The Story of Gideon

$\frac{10}{10} - 0$

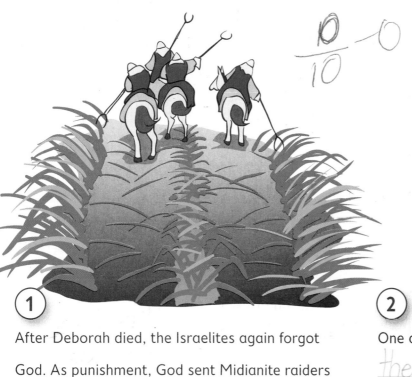

1

After Deborah died, the Israelites again forgot God. As punishment, God sent Midianite raiders who _came into the country and attacked_ .

2

One day an angel told Gideon, "_Mighty warrior the LORD is with you._" Gideon asked for a sign. Draw what happened to the food when the stranger touched it with his staff.

3

Gideon obeyed the angel's command to _strike down all the men of Midian all at one time._ .

4

Gideon asked God to give him a sign that he was to lead Israel. Gideon put a _piece of wool_ on the threshing floor. In the morning it was _wet_ , and the floor was _dry_ . The next morning the _ground_ was wet, and the _wool_ was dry. Gideon believed.

5

Gideon marched to the Midianite camp with an army of _32,000_ men. Gideon sent home the soldiers who were afraid. How many were left? _10,000_

6

God told Gideon to use only the men who cupped their hands to drink water from the river. How many did he use? _300_

7

Draw the three weapons that Gideon gave the soldiers before he led them to a hill above the camp.

8

When Gideon gave the signal, everyone blew the _trumpet_, broke the _jar_, and shouted, " _For the LORD and for Gideon_ !"

46

Gideon Review

Fill out the crossword puzzle on Judges 6–8. When you are finished, unscramble the letters in the boxes with circles, squares, or triangles to fill in the message at the end.

Across

1. God told Gideon to send home the soldiers who _____ by the stream. (7:5–7)
4. Gideon took an army of Israelites to fight against the _____. (7:1)
7. Gideon destroyed the altar to Baal and cut down the _____ pole. (6:25)
8. After Gideon died, the people served _____. (8:33)
9. Gideon overheard one of the enemy soldiers telling a dream about a loaf of _____ bread rolling down the hill and destroying a tent. (7:13)
11. Gideon placed meat and unleavened bread on a rock, where _____ consumed them. (6:21)
12. Gideon asked the people to bring him an _____ from their share of the Midianite plunder. (8:24)

Down

2. Gideon and his soldiers attacked the camp, each armed with a torch, an empty jar, and a _____. (7:16)
3. Gideon named his son _____. (8:31)
4. Gideon came from the tribe of _____. (6:15)
5. God told Gideon to allow all of the soldiers who were _____ to go home. (7:3)
6. Gideon made the people a golden _____. (8:27)
10. God sent an _____ to talk to Gideon. (6:11–12)
11. In response to Gideon's request, God sent dew on the threshing floor but not on the _____ that Gideon had set out. (6:39–40)

The ○○○○○ △△△○△△△ to the ◇◇◇◇.

The Fable of the Trees

BY JOTHAM, SON OF GIDEON

One day the trees set out to find a king. They asked the olive tree to be their king. But the olive tree said, "Why should I give up my olive oil, which people love so much, just to be king of the trees?"

Then the trees came to the grapevine and asked it to be king of the trees. But the grapevine asked, "Why should I give up making wine, which people enjoy so much, just to be king of the trees?"

1

Then the trees asked the fig tree to be king of the trees. But the fig tree replied, "Why should I give up my fruit, which people find so good and sweet, just to be king of the trees?"

Finally the trees came to the thornbush and said, "Please be our king, and rule over us." And the thornbush replied, "If you really want me to be your king, I will. But if you are teasing, let fire come out of me and burn you up!" So the trees made the lowly thornbush their king, and he ruled over them.

2

Jephthah

Name Sonia Lau 1/8/18

#6

Answer the following questions based on Judges 10–12.

1. How did Israel sin against God before he sent the next judge?

They worshiped other gods.

5. How long did Israel live in peace until the judge died?

Israel lived in peace for 6 years.

2. Which of Israel's enemies ruled over them? For how long?

The Philistines and Ammonites ruled for 18 year

4. Whom did God send as a deliverer/judge? What was he like?

Jephthah was rejected by his brothers because his mother was a prostitute. He was a scoundrel

3. What did the people of Israel say when they cried to God?

"We have sinned against you, forsaking our God and serving the Baals.

Samson's Early Blessings

God gave Samson many blessings and advantages as a young man. List as many examples of these blessings as you can.

God also gives us many blessings. Write down as many examples as you can of the blessings God has given you, his special child.

Samson's Revenge

Fill blanks left in the chart below with examples of Samson's revenge. When you are finished, answer the questions on the back of the activity sheet.

1 Samson married a Philistine despite his parents' advice.

2 Samson's wife cried and asked for the answer to a riddle.

3 Samson told his wife the answer, and she told her friends.

4 Samson was angry and went on to ~~Ashkelon his father's home~~ kill thirty men

5 Samson was angry with his wife, so he returned to his father's home

6 Samson's wife was given in marriage to another man.

7 Samson calmed down and decided that he wanted his wife back.

8 Samson found out that his wife had remarried, so he decided that he would get even with the Philistines

9 The Philistines killed Samson's wife and her father.

10 Samson was handed over to the Philistines by the Israelites.

11 Samson escaped and hid in the cave of the rock of Etham, struck down thirty men.

12 What do you think will happen next? He would kill all the Philistine men and be Israel's judge.

1. How did Samson misuse the strength and power that God had given him? _He killed_ many men. He used it to take revenge from other people.

_____

_____

2. How did God bless his people despite Samson's mistakes and vengeance? _____

_____

_____

_____

You Can Be Stronger than Samson

Name _____1/23/18_____

Temptation is a state experienced when a person has thoughts or wishes that are contrary to the will of God.

1. Look up each of the references below, and write in the box what the Bible teaches about temptation.

Scripture reference	What we learn
James 1:14–15	It can lead to death
1 Peter 5:8	Be aware of your enemy (Satan)
1 Corinthians 10:12	Don't be proud
1 Corinthians 10:13	He provides a way out
Hebrews 12:1	Throw off any sin that hinder us
1 Timothy 6:9	A love of money brings temptation
Hebrews 4:15	Jesus was tempted so he understands
James 1:2–3	God might use it to test our faith
Proverbs 4:14–15	Take action to avoid it
Proverbs 13:20	We need to keep good company
James 4:7–8	Growing close to God helps us resist Satan.

2. What could Samson have done differently to avoid temptation? _He could not have married an unbeliever, he should have kept the secret of the Nazirites, and he shouldn't have hung around with the Philistines. He should asked God for help instead of doing it his own way._

3. What can you do to avoid temptation? _I can be aware of what I watch, who my friends are, and who I call-out to._

Shadow Box

You learned about many different people in Samson's story. Choose one character, such as Samson, Delilah, Samson's mother or father, Samson's wife, Samson's father-in-law, or another Philistine. Write the name or identity of the person on top of the box. In the spaces in the memory box/shadow box below, draw five objects that remind you of the character you chose. For example, for Samson, you could draw a barbell to remind you of his strength.

The Danites and the Levites

God gave his commands to the people of Israel at Mount Sinai. In today's story many of God's commands were broken. Circle the number of each command that was broken in today's story. Below the command, write how it was broken.

1. You shall have no other gods before me. _____

2. You shall not make for yourself an idol. _____

3. You shall not misuse the name of the Lord your God. _____

4. Remember the Sabbath day by keeping it holy. _____

5. Honor your father and your mother. _____

6. You shall not murder. _____

7. You shall not commit adultery. _____

8. You shall not steal. _____

9. You shall not give false testimony against your neighbor. _____

10. You shall not covet. _____

Name _____

Downward Spiral of the Judges

Fill in the blanks by reading the verses from the Book of Judges. Then cut out the spiral and hold it by the top. What happens?

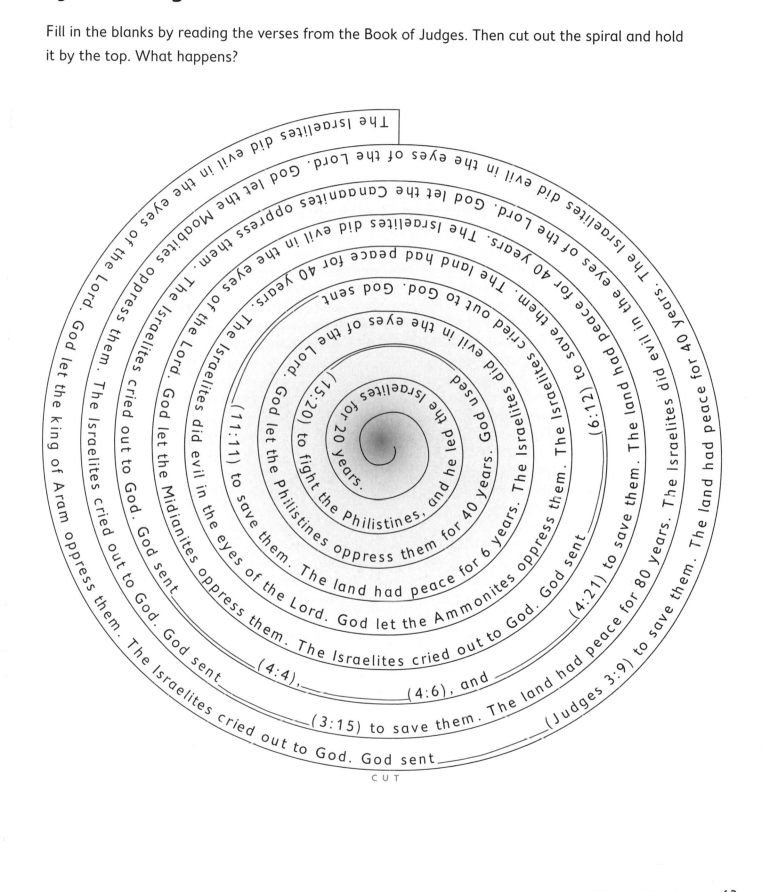

The Israelites did evil in the eyes of the Lord. God let the Moabites oppress them. The Israelites cried out to God. God let the king of Aram oppress them. The Israelites cried out to God. God sent _____ (4:4), _____ (4:6), and _____ (3:15) to save them. The Israelites cried out to God. God sent _____ (Judges 3:9) to save them. The land had peace for 80 years. The Israelites did evil in the eyes of the Lord. God let the Canaanites oppress them. The Israelites did evil in the eyes of the Lord. God let the Israelites did evil in the eyes of the Lord. God let the Midianites oppress them. The Israelites cried out to God. God let the Philistines oppress them for 40 years. The land had peace for 40 years. God let the Ammonites oppress them. The Israelites cried out to God. God sent _____ (4:21) to save them. The land had peace for 40 years. The Israelites cried out to God. God sent _____ (6:12) to save them. The land had peace for 6 years. The Israelites did evil in the eyes of the Lord. God let the Philistines oppress them for 20 years. (15:20) to fight the Philistines, and he led the Israelites for 20 years. God used _____ (11:11) to save them. The land had peace for 40 years.

CUT

Ruth and Naomi

Name _____ 1/30/18

15/15

Use the clues on the following page and Ruth 1 to fill in the answers to the puzzle.
The box will give you the theme of this lesson.

1 R u t h
2 J u d g e s
3 B e t h l e h e m
4 M a h l o n
5 E l i m e l e c h
6 O r p a h
7 f o o d
8 h o m e
9 m o t h e r ' s
10 w e p t
11 s t a y
12 G o d
13 t w o
14 d a u g h t e r - i n - l a w

Clues:

1. The leading character in this book of the Bible is _Ruth_.

2. The story of Ruth takes place during the time of the _Judges_.

3. Elimelech and his family left the famine in _Bethlehem_ and went to Moab.

4. Elimelech's sons were _Mahlon_ and Kilion.

5. Naomi's husband, _Elimelech_, died.

6. In Moab the sons married _Orpah_ and Ruth.

7. Naomi heard there was _oppresion_ again in Israel.

8. She and her daughters-in-law prepared to return _home_.

9. "Go back to your _mother's_ home," Naomi told them.

10. They all _wept_ and Orpah kissed Naomi good-bye.

11. Ruth insisted, "Where you go I will go, and where you _stay_ I will _stay_."

12. "Your people will be my people and your _God_ my _God_."

13. The _two_ women went on until they came to Bethlehem.

14. Naomi and her _daughter in law_ arrived as the barley harvest was beginning.

Ruth Meets Boaz

Ruth 2

Ruth: Mother, it is harvest time. I know what the law says. The harvesters will leave grain for us widows. Let me go find someone who will let me stay and glean in his field.

Naomi: It is not easy work, but go ahead, my daughter. We need to eat!

Narrator: Ruth ended up in the field of Boaz, a relative of Elimelech. She worked throughout the day. Boaz arrived and was greeting the harvesters.

Boaz: The Lord be with you!

Harvesters: The Lord bless you!

Boaz: What a great harvest the Lord has given this year! You are leaving grain for our neighbors?

Foreman: Of course, sir. There are plenty of gleaners today!

Boaz: Who is that woman? I haven't seen her before.

Foreman: She is the Moabite, Ruth, who came back with Naomi. She has been working diligently all day!

Narrator: Boaz went over to Ruth.

Boaz: Greetings! Welcome to my field. Be sure to stay here to glean. You'll be safe here. If you're thirsty, just help yourself to those water jars over there.

Ruth: Sir, why are you being so kind to me, a foreigner?

Boaz: Ruth, your reputation precedes you. I have heard of your kindness to Naomi and of your desire to follow the God of Israel. May the Lord repay you for all that you have done.

Ruth: Thank you, sir. You have been so kind to your servant.

Boaz: Ruth, would you like to eat with me at lunchtime?

Ruth: Why, thank you.

Boaz: I'll see you then. Meet me by the water jars.

Narrator: After lunch, Boaz had some special instructions for his men.

Boaz: When Ruth is gleaning, leave some extra heads of grain for her. Don't stop her from taking all she wants. But don't tell her I told you to do this!

Foreman: Yes, sir.

Narrator: At the end of the day, Ruth returned home with a lot of grain!

Naomi: Ruth, you must be so tired. Come sit down. Oh my! Look at all the grain.

Ruth: Oh Mother, I had the most wonderful day. The owner of the field was so kind to me, and everyone took care of me so well. Just look at all this food!

Naomi: I can't believe it! Who was the owner of this field?

Ruth: His name was Boaz.

Naomi: Praise be to God! He has not forgotten us! Boaz is a close relative of ours. Ruth, I know that God will look after us. You just wait and see!

God Honors Character

Name _____ 2/2/18

Beside each picture, write at least one characteristic of Boaz or Ruth.

1. Ruth clings to Naomi as Orpah leaves.

   determined
   willing

5. Ruth returns home to Naomi with grain.

   happy
   giving
   hardworking
   generous

2. Ruth walks to Bethlehem with Naomi.

   brave

6. Boaz greets his workers.

   kind
   thoughtful

3. Ruth gleans in the field.

   hardworking

7. Boaz asks his foreman about Ruth.

   unsure
   curious
   caring
   helpful
   kind

4. Ruth has lunch with Boaz.

   loving kind
   Selfless
   nice

8. Boaz directs his workers to leave grain for Ruth.

   caring
   giving
   sharing
   loving
   thoughtful

Ruth and Boaz

Name _____

Number the following events in order as they occurred in Ruth 3 and 4.

Ruth 3

_7_ Boaz gave Ruth six measures of barley.

_5_ Ruth asked Boaz to spread his garment over her.

_3_ Ruth quietly uncovered Boaz's feet and lay down.

_1_ Naomi wanted to find a home for Ruth with Boaz.

_8_ Ruth told Naomi all that had happened.

_2_ Ruth obeyed Naomi and went to the threshing floor.

_4_ Boaz woke up in the night, startled.

_6_ Boaz told Ruth that there was a closer relative.

Ruth 4

_8_ The witnesses at the city gate blessed Boaz and Ruth.

_1_ Boaz went to the city gate.

_5_ The closer relative no longer wanted the land and told Boaz to redeem it.

_2_ Boaz asked the closer relative if he wanted to redeem Elimelech's land.

_7_ Boaz announced in front of the elders that he had acquired the land and Ruth.

_3_ "I will redeem it," the closer relative said.

_6_ A sandal was given to legalize the transaction.

_4_ Boaz explained that the redeemer would also marry the widow Ruth.

Jesus, Our Kinsman-Redeemer

Name _____2/6/18_____

Look up the Scriptures and make a comparison.
Write what we learn about our Kinsman-Redeemer, Jesus Christ.

1. Ruth was a Moabitess, not an Israelite, and not under God's covenantal relationship.	Ephesians 2:12 Without Christ, we are like foreigners.
2. Naomi accepted and loved her daughters-in-law, even though they weren't from Israel.	Romans 5:8 God loves us very much, He sent Jesus Christ to die for our sins.
3. Boaz showed kindness to Ruth.	1 John 3:1 God loves us very much, Heaven calls us children of God.
4. Boaz covered Ruth with his garment.	Psalm 91:4 God protects us from Satan.
5. Boaz redeemed the parcel of land as the law demanded so that he might restore it to Naomi.	Galatians 4:4–5 God redeem us as his children us as his children,
6. Boaz publicly made a transaction to redeem Ruth.	John 12:32–33 Jesus Christ publicly died on the cross.
7. Boaz had to pay the price in full.	1 Peter 1:18–19 Jesus paid us for our sins with his blood.
8. Ruth was blessed because Boaz paid the price of redemption.	Colossians 1:12–14 Jesus accepted us to his kingdom.

Ruth's Family Tree

Turn to Ruth 4:18–22 and fill in the family tree of Ruth.

Perez

Hezron

Ram

Amminadab

Nahshon

Salmon

Booz

Obed

Jesse

David

"My Story" by Hannah

I am Hannah. I praised the LORD and asked the Lord. I made a vow saying, "If you would give me a son, Lord, I will devote him to the LORD all the days of his life, and no razor would be used on his head." The LORD gave me a son, named Samuel. I weaned him until he was three years old. Then, I took him to the Temple of the LORD in Shiloh, where he would be devoted to the LORD all the days in his life. There, the priest Eli would care for the baby, and live there always. I am glad that the LORD has heard me when I was unhappy.

P.S. The priest Eli thought I was drunk! (Many people in this time disobeys the LORD, not a good thing.)

Samuel's Birth and Calling

Name _____ 3/12/16

Find the answers for this crossword puzzle in the Book of 1 Samuel.

Across

4. Hannah brought this to her son every year. (2:19)
5. God continued to do this to Samuel at Shiloh. (3:21)
7. Hannah named her son this. (1:20)
10. Eli's sons were described this way. (2:12)
11. _____ times, Samuel thought it was Eli who had been calling. (3:8)
14. God did this to Samuel in the night. (3:4)
18. Hannah quietly prayed at this place. (1:9, see footnote)
19. A man of God made this against the house of Eli. (2:27–36)
20. Hannah went with her husband yearly to this place of worship. (1:3)

Down

1. Hannah gave her son back to him. (1:28)
2. All Israel recognized Samuel as this. (3:20)
3. Eli's sons did not listen to their father's _____. (2:25)
6. God said he would do this to Eli's family. (3:13)
8. This person thought Hannah was drunk. (1:13)
9. Samuel felt this way about telling Eli the message. (3:15)
10. The family did this before heading home. (1:19)
12. The boy did this before the Lord under Eli. (2:11)
13. Hannah's prayer was full of this. (2:1)
14. Eli's sons treated the Lord's offering with this. (2:17)
15. He was the husband of both Hannah and Peninnah. (1:1–2)
16. He was Hophni's brother. (2:34)
17. There were not many of these in the days of Eli. (3:1)

The Capture of the Ark

Name _____

Narrator 1: The Israelites went out to fight the Philistines at Ebenezer.

Narrator 2: The Philistines defeated them and killed 4,000 Israelites on the battlefield.

Soldier 1: How could God let us be defeated like this?

Soldier 2: I thought that God hated the Philistines as much as we do!

Captain: Wait a minute. I think I know what the problem is.

Soldier 2: What?

Captain: We need to do more than just call on God in our prayers and offer him sacrifices.

Soldier 1: What do you mean?

Captain: We need to bring God here—out onto the battlefield.

Soldier 2: How are we supposed to do that?

Captain: We need to bring the ark of the covenant from Shiloh and take it to battle with us. If the ark is here, then God will be here.

Narrator 3: So they sent word to Eli's sons, Hophni and Phinehas, to bring the ark to the camp.

Narrator 1: The Israelites thought that the ark was a lucky charm that would save them from their enemies. They forgot that the ark was a reminder to the people that God was dwelling with them.

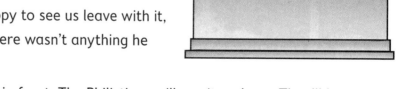

Hophni: Here it is! Just as you ordered.

Phinehas: Where do you want us to put it?

Hophni: Father wasn't too happy to see us leave with it, but he's so old that there wasn't anything he could do to stop us.

Captain: Let's put the ark right in front. The Philistines will see it and run. They'll be so scared—we won't even need to fight!

Phinehas: Are you sure you want it in front? What if they capture it?

Captain: Capture it? Are you crazy? Now that we have God right here with us there's no way the Philistines can win.

Hophni: Well, get going. Father is sitting by the road waiting for news of our victory.

Phinehas: He's going to want that ark back soon, so hurry up.

Captain: Israelites, are you ready for battle?

Israelites:	Yes, sir!
Captain:	And what's your battle cry?
Israelites:	We've got the ark! We've got the ark! We've got the ark!
Narrator 3:	The ark was taken into battle with the Israelites.
Narrator 1:	The Philistines were afraid of this new power that the Israelites seemed to have.
Narrator 2:	But God was not with the Israelites, and the Philistines defeated them.
Messenger:	Eli, I have some terrible news. Hophni and Phinehas were killed in the battle, and the Philistines captured the ark.
Narrator 3:	When Eli heard this, he fell backward off his chair. His neck broke, and he died.
Narrator 2:	The Philistines took the ark to the temple of Dagon, their chief god. They wanted to thank Dagon for the victory over the Israelites.
Priest 1:	Well, it's time to open the temple. The worshipers will be arriving soon.
Priest 2:	The people have a lot to be thankful for today.
Priest 1:	They sure do. We defeated those pesky Israelites and captured their God.
Priest 2:	I wonder how their God liked bowing down to Dagon all night. I wish the Israelites could have seen that.
Priest 1:	Well, open the doors, and let the people in.
Priest 2:	Oh, no!
Priest 1:	~~What?~~ Vat!
Priest 2:	Something is wrong with Dagon.
Priest 1:	How can anything be wrong with Dagon?
Priest 2:	Look.
Priest 1:	This is horrible! Dagon is bowing down to the God of Israel.
Priest 2:	And his hands are broken off!
Priest 1:	That's not the worst of it. He's headless too!
Priest 2:	What are we going to tell the people? We can't let them see Dagon like this. They'll never worship him again.
Priest 1:	It's that ark. We never should have brought it here.
Priest 2:	Let's get rid of it—now!
Adad:	Hey, priests!
Priest 1:	What is it, young man?

Adad:	We've got a problem. People throughout the city have sores popping out all over their bodies.
Priest 2:	When did this start?
Adad:	As soon as the men returned from battle, people started getting sick.
Priest 1:	It's that ark. The Israelites' God is more powerful than we thought.
Priest 2:	Let's ask the people what they want to do with this battle trophy.
Priest 1:	People of Philistia, what do you want to do with the Israelites' ark?
Philistines:	Send it away! Send it away!
Narrator 1:	The Philistines sent the ark from city to city.
Narrator 2:	But wherever the ark went, the people became sick.
Narrator 3:	Finally the Philistines sent the ark back to Israel, along with a variety of gifts.
Narrator 1:	They never wanted see the ark again.
Narrator 2:	The ark was returned to Israel, but it never again returned to Shiloh.

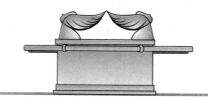

The Philistines Take the Ark

Name _Sonia Lau 3/17/16 #6_

1 Samuel 4–6 tells of how the ark was taken from Israel and later returned. Use the Bible to find the answers to the following questions. Circle the letter in front of the correct answer.

The Ark Is Taken

1. Why was the ark taken into the battle? (4:1–4)

   A. Samuel told the army to take it.

   F. Israel wouldn't stop shouting until it came.

   C. The Israelites thought that it would help them win the battle.

2. How did God punish the Israelites for this sin? (4:5–11)

   A. He let the Philistines win the battle and take the ark.

   Q. He sent plagues to destroy the Israelites' animals.

   E. He made the Israelites become sick.

3. How did Eli die? (4:12–18)

   L. When he heard that the ark had been taken, he fell backward and broke his neck.

   M. The Philistines killed him.

   O. His sons killed him after they lost the battle.

4. Why did Phinehas's wife name her son Ichabod? (4:19–22)

   P. She named her son after her father.

   B. Ichabod means "the ark of God has been captured."

   L. Ichabod means "the glory has departed from Israel."

The Ark Is in Philistia

5. What happened when the Philistines put the ark in Dagon's temple? (5:1–5)

   E. Dagon fell on his face before the ark.

   U. Dagon stayed in his usual place.

   W. The doorway in the temple broke.

6. How did God punish each of the cities where the ark was sent? (5:6–12)

  A. All of the people in the cities died.

  D. The people got tumors.

  F. The soldiers lost all of their battles.

The Ark Is Returned

7. Why did the Philistines send offerings with the ark? (6:1–8)

  A. They knew that the Israelites were poor after losing many battles.

  B. They wanted to please the Israelites' God.

  C. They hoped that the Israelites would leave them alone from now on.

8. To what place was the ark taken? (6:9–12)

  Y. Beth Shemesh.

  D. Egypt.

  H. Philistia.

9. How did the people there react to the ark's return? (6:13–18)

  I. They wept at the sight of the ark.

  G. They rejoiced and brought sacrifices.

  M. They said that didn't want it.

10. Why were 70 of the people punished? (6:19–20)

  O. They looked into the ark.

  E. They had let the Philistines capture the ark.

  U. They were angry with God.

11. Where did the ark finally stay? (6:21—7:1)

  D. At Abinadab's house in Kiriath Jearim.

  M. In Beth Shemesh.

  P. At Eleazar's house.

Now that you have circled all of the correct answers, write the circled letters in order in the following boxes. The message will tell you something important about Samuel.

  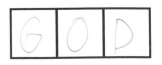

Important Cities

Name _____ 4/2/18

Find the names of the important cities during Samuel's time by looking up these Scripture passages from the Book of 1 Samuel. Look at where each city is located on the map.

1. The Israelites camped here.

   (4:1–2)

   Ebenezer

2. The Philistines camped here.

   (4:1–2)

   Aphek

3. The ark was here before the

   Israelites took it to Ebenezer.

   (4:3)

   Shiloh

4. The ark was taken to Dagon's

   temple here. (5:1–2)

   Ashdod

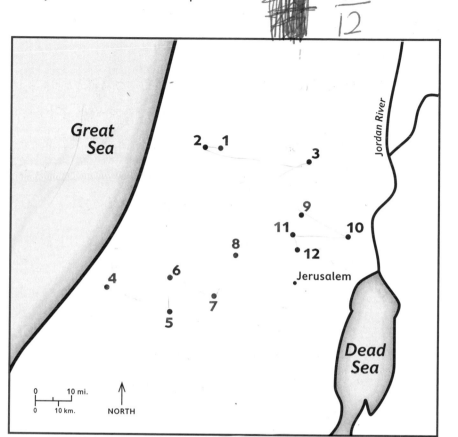

5. After the ark was taken here, the

   people became sick. (5:8–9) *Gath*

6. People refused to let the ark come here. (5:10–12) *Ekron*

7. The ark was returned to Israel here. People looked inside the ark and died.

   (6:13–16, 19) *Beth Shemesh*

8. The ark stayed here for 20 years. (6:21—7:1) *Kiriath Jearim*

9. This was the first city in Samuel's circuit each year. (7:16) *Bethel*

10. This was the second city in Samuel's yearly circuit. (7:16) *Gilgal*

11. This was the third city in Samuel's yearly circuit. (7:16) *Mizpah*

12. This city was Samuel's home. (7:17) *Ramah*

Christ's Sacrifice

Jesus offered himself as a sacrifice for our sins. Romans 12:1 says, "Therefore, I urge you, brothers, in view of God's mercy, to offer your bodies as living sacrifices, holy and pleasing to God—this is your spiritual act of worship." We no longer need to offer sacrifices of animals or grain. Instead, we are to offer ourselves as living sacrifices to God. In the squares on the rock, write ways that you can show others that you are a living sacrifice for God.

At school
- Show respect to classmates and teachers
- Be kind to others
- Work hard now

At home
- Obey and do my best for my parents
- Obey
- Do chores without whining
- serve of

In the community
- Show others about Christ
- Being respectful and kind
- serve others

With friends
- Be helpful and kind
- Teach them the gospel
- Correct them if they are wrong

At church
- willing to praise the Lord
- sing gospel
- stay focused on God

In sports and other activities
- be a good sport
- do your best not to win
- be encouraging

Warning! Warning!

Name _____4/4/18_____ #6

God warned the people of what would happen if they had a king. Use 1 Samuel 8 15/15 to help you list the problems that having a king would bring to the people.

A king would take sons, and make them serve with his chariots and horses, take the sons and be commanders of many men, some will plow his fields and gather the crops, and others will have to make weapons and chariot parts for war. The king would take daughters, they will make perfume, bake and cook. The king will take the best fields, vineyards, and olive groves, to give them to his attendants. He will take a tenth of all the people's grapes, sheep, and goats. The king will take male and female servants. He will take their best cattle and donkeys. He will make the people servants. When they cry out to the Lord, the Lord will not answer.

God warns that disobedience will lead to negative consequences for us as well. Read the following passages and state the warning you find there. (The first one is done for you.)

1. Deuteronomy 18:10 ___Have nothing to do with witchcraft.___
2. Psalm 37:8 _Don't be upset, and don't be angry_
3. Hosea 4:6 _Don't ignore or refuse to God's law_
4. Matthew 6:15 _God will not forgive you sins if you do not forgive others sins_
5. Matthew 24:44 _The Lord will come at a time you don't expect_
6. John 15:5–6 _You can never do anything without God_
7. 2 Corinthians 11:13–14 _Do not be a false apostle and serve Satan. God has a punishment_
8. 1 Peter 3:9 _Don't be proud, do not say unkind words._
9. 1 Peter 5:8 _Control youseves, guard yourself_
10. Revelation 22:18–19 _Do not add or take away any thing from the Bible._

The Anointing of Saul

Name _____

We Want a King—1 Samuel 8

1. Read 1 Samuel 8:1–3. How were Samuel's sons like Eli's sons?
   They were doing evil and weren't following his father's way.

2. Read 1 Samuel 8:4–9. What did Samuel do when the people requested a king?
   Samuel prayed to the Lord.

   What was God's response? _God told Samuel to listen to them and give them a king. He told Samuel to warn them about the troubles of having a king._

3. Read 1 Samuel 8:10–18. God warned the people of what would happen if they had a king.

   List the problems that having a king would bring to the people. _God will take the people's sons and make them work with chariots and horses, and be commanders, others to do harvest and make war equipment. He will take the daughters and make them purfumers and bakers. He will take the best of the vineyards and fields._

4. Read 1 Samuel 8:19–22. Why did the people want a king? _The people wanted a king because all the other nations had a king to lead and rule over them and fight for them._

Anointing a King—1 Samuel 9:1—10:8

1. What do you learn about Saul from 1 Samuel 9:1–2? _Saul was a son of Kish, and he was a young man._

2. Read 1 Samuel 9:3–6. How did God arrange for Saul to travel to the town where Samuel was staying? _The servant told Saul to go to Samuel for help._

3. Read 1 Samuel 9:15–27. How did Samuel learn who would be Israel's first king? _God told Samuel about Saul._

How did Samuel treat Saul at their first meeting? *Samuel treated Saul respectfully.*

How did Saul react to the treatment he received from Samuel? *Saul was not respectfull.*

4. Read 1 Samuel 10:1–8. What did Samuel do to Saul before he left? *Samuel tells Saul instructions for God to always be with him.*

What did Samuel say would happen to Saul on his trip home? *Saul would meet two men. The men would tell him that the donkey was found Then, he would meet three men, and he would take two of the 3 loaves of bread. After that, Saul will meet people prophesying.*

Why do you think God gave Saul these three signs? *God gave them these three signs to show he was trustworthy.*

Presenting the King—1 Samuel 10:9–27

1. Read 1 Samuel 10:17–19. What final reminder did Samuel give the people before giving them a king? *He reminded them about all the things God had done for them.*

2. Read 1 Samuel 10:20–22. Where did the people find Saul when Samuel chose his name as the king of Israel? *He was hiding among the supplies.*

3. Read 1 Samuel 10:23–27. What did the people think of their new king? *The people were excited and happy. Some people did not like Saul.*

Where did Saul go to live after he became king? *Saul went back to his home in Gibeah.*

What did Saul say or do to those who did not want him to be king? *Saul kept silent.*

The Anointing of Saul

Name _____ 5/2/18

Find the answers for this crossword puzzle in the Book of 1 Samuel.

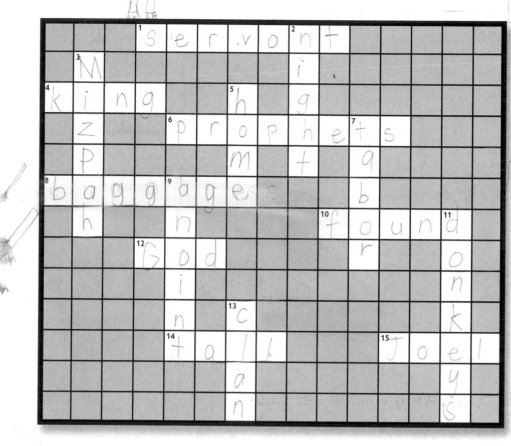

Across

1. Saul's _____ suggested that they ask the prophet Samuel for help in finding their missing animals. (9:6)
4. The people of Israel asked Samuel for a _____. (8:6)
6. Samuel told Saul that he would see a procession of _____. (10:5)
8. Saul, a humble person, hid among the _____. (10:22)
10. Samuel told Saul that the missing animals had been _____. (9:20)
12. _____ told Samuel to give the people a king. (8:22)
14. Saul was an unusually _____ man. (9:2)
15. Samuel's dishonest sons were named _____ and Abijah. (8:2)

Down

2. Saul stayed at Samuel's house for one _____. (9:25–26)
3. Samuel called the Israelites to _____ to announce their king. (10:17).
5. After Saul became king, he went to his _____ in Gibeah. (10:26)
7. Samuel told Saul that he would be met at the tree of _____ by three men, who would give him food. (10:3–4)
9. God told Samuel to _____ Saul king over Israel. (9:15–16)
11. Saul was searching for his father's _____ when he met Samuel. (9:3)
13. Saul was surprised to be invited to the feast because he was not from an important _____. (9:21)

Samuel's Farewell

Samuel gave the people of Israel this final advice: "Be sure to fear the LORD and serve him faithfully with all your heart; consider what great things he has done for you" (1 Samuel 12:24). This is also good advice for us. In the hearts write down and draw a picture or symbol of some of the great things that God has done for you.

He VII

The Rejected King

$\frac{7}{7}$

Saul's Fear

1. Read 1 Samuel 13:1–8. What was the response of Saul and his army to the huge army of the Philistines? _Saul and his army was afraid of the Philistine's large army._

Saul's Disobedience

2. Read 1 Samuel 13:8–15. How did Saul disobey God? _Saul disobeyed God. He burnt the burnt offerings without Saul._

3. Read 1 Samuel 15:1–12. Write down the ways that Saul was disobedient to God in his victory over the Amalekites. _Saul kept the king of the Amalekites alive. He was supposed to kill and destroy every Amalekites and the things that belonged to them. He kept the best of the cattle and sheep alive. He made a monument of his own honor._

Saul's Excuses

4. Read 1 Samuel 15:13–25. What excuses did Saul make to Samuel for not destroying all of the Amalekites? _Saul said to Samuel that he did obey God, and he destroyed all the Amalekites, but he saved the best of animals to sacrifice to God._

Saul's Punishment

5. Read 1 Samuel 15:26–35. How did Samuel complete what God had commanded Saul to do?

   He killed Agag.

6. What punishment did Samuel announce to Saul in both these accounts of his disobedience?

   He will lose his kingship

7. What was Saul and Samuel's relationship like for the rest of Samuel's life?

   He mourned for Saul, and he was sad.

What
was
Saul
and
Samuel's
relationship
like
for
the
rest
of
Samuel's
life
?

Jonathan and the Philistines

Name _____

Part 1—Jonathan's Daring Plan

Narrator 1: One day Jonathan was with the young man who carried his armor.

Jonathan: Let's go over to where the Philistines have their outpost.

Narrator 1: Jonathan did not tell his father, Saul, what he was doing.

Narrator 2: Meanwhile, Saul and his 600 men were camped on the outskirts of Gibeah.

Narrator 3: No one realized that Jonathan had left the Israelite camp.

Jonathan: Let's go across to see those pagans. Maybe God will help us. He can win a battle whether he has many warriors or only a few!

Armor-bearer: Do what you think is best. I will be with you whatever you decide.

Jonathan: Then we will cross over and let them see us. If they say, "Stay where you are or we'll kill you," then we will stop and not go up to them. But if they say, "Come on up and fight," then we will go up. That will be God's sign that he will help us defeat them.

Narrator 2: The Philistines saw them coming.

Philistines: Look! The Hebrews are crawling out of their holes! Come on up here, and we'll teach you a lesson!

Jonathan: Come on, climb right behind me, for God will help us defeat them!

Narrator 4: So they climbed up, and the Philistines fell back as Jonathan and his armor-bearer killed them right and left. They killed about 20 men in all.

Narrator 1: Suddenly, panic broke out in the Philistine army. Just then an earthquake struck, and everyone was terrified.

Narrator 2: Saul's lookouts in Gibeah saw a strange sight—the vast army of Philistines began to melt away in every direction.

Saul: Find out who isn't here!

Narrator 3: When they checked, they found that Jonathan and his armor-bearer were gone.

Narrator 2: Saul and his 600 men rushed out to the battle and found the Philistines killing each other. There was terrible confusion everywhere. Even the Hebrews who had gone over to the Philistine army revolted and joined in with Saul, Jonathan, and the rest of the Israelites.

Narrator 3: The men who had been hiding in the hills joined the chase when they saw the Philistines running away. So the Lord saved Israel that day.

Part 2—Saul's Foolish Oath

Narrator 1: The men of Israel were worn out that day, because Saul had made them take an oath.

Saul: Let a curse fall on anyone who eats before evening—before I have full revenge on my enemies.

Narrator 2: So no one ate a thing all day, even though they found a honeycomb on the ground in the forest. They didn't even touch the honey, because they all feared the oath they had taken.

Narrator 3: But Jonathan had not heard his father's command, and he dipped a stick into a piece of honeycomb and ate the honey. After he had eaten it, he felt much better. But one of the men saw him.

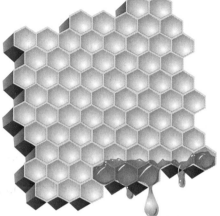

Man: Your father made the army take a strict oath that anyone who eats food today will be cursed. That is why everyone is weary and faint.

Jonathan: My father has made trouble for us all! A command like that only hurts us. See how much better I look now that I have eaten this little bit of honey. If the men had been allowed to eat freely from the food they found among our enemies, think how many more we could have killed!

Narrator 4: But hungry as they were, they chased and killed the Philistines all day, growing more and more faint.

Narrator 1: That evening they pounced on the battle plunder and butchered the sheep, cattle, and calves, but they ate them without draining the blood.

Man: Look, the men are sinning against the Lord by eating meat that still has blood in it.

Saul: That is very wrong. Find a large stone and roll it over here. Then go out among the troops and tell them, "Bring the cattle and sheep here to kill them and drain the blood. Do not sin against the Lord by eating meat with the blood still in it."

Narrator 2: So that night all the troops brought their animals and slaughtered them there. And Saul built an altar to the Lord, the first one he had ever built.

Saul: Let's chase the Philistines all night and destroy every last one of them.

Men: We'll do whatever you think is best.

Priest: Let's ask God first.

Saul:	God, should we go after the Philistines? Will you help us defeat them?
Narrator 4:	But God made no reply that day.
Saul:	Something's wrong. I want all my army commanders to come here. We must find out what sin was committed today. I vow by the name of the Lord who rescued Israel that the sinner will surely die, even if it is my own son Jonathan!
Narrator 3:	But no one would tell him what the trouble was.
Saul:	Jonathan and I will stand over here and all of you stand over there.
Narrator 1:	And all the people agreed. Then Saul prayed.
Saul:	O Lord, God of Israel, please tell us who is guilty and who is innocent. Are Jonathan and I guilty, or is the sin among the others?
Narrator 2:	Jonathan and Saul were chosen as the guilty ones, and the people were declared innocent.
Saul:	Now choose between me and Jonathan.
Narrator 3:	Jonathan was shown to be the guilty one.
Saul:	Tell me what you have done.
Jonathan:	I tasted a little honey; it was only a little bit on the end of a stick. Does that deserve death?
Saul:	Yes, Jonathan, you must die! May God strike me dead if you are not executed for this.
Men:	Should Jonathan, who saved Israel today, die? Far from it! As surely as the Lord lives, not a hair on his head will be touched, for he has been used of God to do a mighty miracle today.
Narrator 4:	So the people rescued Jonathan, and he was not put to death. Then Saul called back the army from chasing the Philistines, and the Philistines returned home.

Name _____

5/5/18 #6

$$\frac{15}{16} \quad -1$$

Saul Wins Battles but Loses the Kingship

Fill in the blanks in the story below.
If you need help, turn to 1 Samuel 13–14.

1 After Saul's son Jonathan successfully attacked them at Geba, the Philistines gathered an army of 3000 chariots and 6000 charioteers to fight the Israelites, who had 3000 soldiers.

2 The Israelites heard about the army, and many of them scattered. Saul saw this and didn't want to wait any longer for Samuel to come and make a sacrifice, so Saul did it himself.

3 One day, Jonathan and his armor-bearer attacked the Philistine outpost. They fought so bravely that the Philistines ran.

4 When Saul saw what was happening, he and his army persued the Philistines. God gave Israel victory.

5 Israel's soldiers were exhausted! They hadn't eaten all day because of a foolish oath that King Saul had made. Jonathan wasn't aware of this and ate some honey. The men had to stop Saul from killing Jonathan.

Training to Be a Child of the King

During David's early life, God was training him to be Israel's next king. God wanted a godly man to lead his people. In the same way, God wants you to train to be his child. On the pieces of athletic equipment below, write down ways that you can train to be a child of the King.

David and Goliath

Narrator 1: Once again the Philistines and Israelites gathered to fight. The Philistines camped on one end of the Valley of Elah, and the Israelites camped on the other end.

Narrator 2: The Philistines had hired a champion named Goliath. Goliath stood over nine feet tall.

Narrator 3: Goliath wore a bronze helmet. His armor weighed 125 pounds, and he carried a spear with an iron point that weighed 15 pounds.

Philistine soldier 1: Hey, buddy, what time is it?

Philistine soldier 2: It's time to watch some scaredy-cat Israelites run into their tents again.

Philistine soldier 3: Hey, Goliath, it's showtime.

Goliath: Just a minute. I'm practicing a new fierce expression. What do you think of this? (Goliath makes a scary face.)

Philistine soldier 4: Are you trying to scare them or make them laugh?

Goliath: You mean you don't find that frightening?

Philistine soldier 4: No. I think you'd better stick with the old one. Just show your teeth and growl. That sends them running every time.

Goliath: Armor-bearer, do you have my spear and sword?

Armor-bearer: Yes, sir! But do you think you could carry the sword this time? My back hurt after I carried it yesterday.

Goliath: Hey, that's a good idea. I'll carry the sword and lift it over my head as I yell. That would be a good addition to my act. We've been doing this for over a month, and I'm ready to try something new.

Narrator 1: Goliath strode out from the Philistine camp and stood in the valley. He lifted his sword over his head and yelled.

Goliath: I challenge you weakling Israelites to choose a man to fight with me. If he's able to kill me, we will become your slaves; but if I kill him, you will become our slaves. I challenge you to find a man who is worthy to fight with me, the great Goliath of Gath.

Narrator 2:	No soldier in the Israelite army came close in size or strength to Goliath. The terrified Israelites ran into their tents and shook with fear.
Goliath and Philistine soldiers:	(laughter and various insults)
Narrator 3:	Goliath returned to the Philistine camp to relax until the next day, when he would enter the valley and challenge the Israelites again.
Narrator 2:	Jesse, David's father, had three sons serving King Saul in the Israelite army.
Narrator 1:	David went back and forth between King Saul's camp and his father's home in Bethlehem.
Jesse:	David, would you please take this bread to your brothers in the camp?
David:	Yes, Father. I'm sure they would enjoy some food from home.
Jesse:	I'd also like you to take these cheeses to the commander of the unit.
David:	I'll leave right away.
Jesse:	Get some news about your brothers. Find out if they are really doing as well as they want me to believe.
Narrator 3:	David took the bread, cheese, and other supplies as his father had asked. He reached the camp as the army was ready to go out to its battle position, shouting the war cry.
Israelite army:	Victory to Israel! Victory to Israel!
Narrator 1:	The Israelites and the Philistines stood in lines facing each other.
Narrator 3:	The armies did not plan to fight each other that day. They were just trying to show how strong they were.
Narrator 2:	David left his supplies with a guard and ran into the battle lines to find his brothers.
Narrator 3:	As David was talking with his bothers, Goliath stepped out from the Philistine lines and shouted his usual words.
Goliath:	Does anyone over there dare to fight me today? I can't believe you call yourself an army!
Narrator 1:	As soon as Goliath spoke, the Israelite soldiers ran back to their tents to hide.
Israelite soldier 1:	This has to stop. I'm sick of running every time that overgrown monster opens his mouth.
Israelite soldier 2:	Well, if you're so tired of it, why don't you do something about it? You'd get those big rewards from King Saul.

David:	Rewards? What rewards?
Israelite soldier 3:	King Saul has promised to give his oldest daughter in marriage to the man who defeats Goliath.
Israelite soldier 4:	That's not all. He's going to give the soldier a sackful of money, too. And the man and his family will never have to pay taxes again!
Narrator 1:	David spoke with the soldiers, asking them more about Goliath and about King Saul's promises.
David:	Hmm. Who does Goliath think he is anyway, trying to scare God's army?
Eliab:	Who do you think you are that you can just come down here whenever you want?
Abinidab:	Take it easy, Eliab. He's just a kid.
Eliab:	Who's taking care of the sheep while the big, brave David is talking to the soldiers?
Shammah:	Calm down. We don't want the commander to come over here.
Eliab:	You sure do think you're big stuff, David. You think you can just come down here, watch the battle, and figure out what's wrong with the army.
David:	Now what have I done? I was only asking a few questions.
Narrator 1:	Some of King Saul's soldiers reported to him that a young man was asking questions about fighting Goliath. Saul sent for David.
Saul:	I heard that you've been asking questions about the reward that will be given to the man who defeats Goliath.
David:	Yes, sir, I have. Let no one lose heart because of that Philistine. I, the king's servant, will go and fight him.
Saul:	Are you crazy? You can't fight Goliath. You're just a boy! Goliath has been killing men longer than you've been alive.
David:	I know. But I once fought a lion who tried to attack my sheep, and I defeated him. Another time I rescued a sheep from a bear. If God could help me kill these animals, he will surely help me defeat this Philistine who defies God's army. I know that God will keep me safe.
Saul:	Go ahead. I'm convinced. The Lord be with you.
Narrator 2:	Saul dressed David in his own armor and gave him his sword. But Saul's armor was far too large and clumsy for David.
Narrator 3:	David took off Saul's armor. David wore the clothes of a shepherd and carried his sling with him.

Narrator 1:	As David approached the valley where he would meet Goliath, he picked up five smooth stones that were about the size of baseballs.
Narrator 3:	Goliath was told that an Israelite champion had finally been chosen to fight with him.
Narrator 2:	Goliath and his armor-bearer entered the valley and approached David.
Narrator 1:	Goliath was shocked and insulted when he saw that the Israelite champion was only a young boy.
Goliath:	Am I a dog, that you come to me with sticks? I'm not going to play fetch with you. You're just a kid—and a scrawny one at that. Come here. I'll kill you quickly and feed your flesh to the birds and beasts. That will teach you Israelites to take me seriously.
David:	You think that you're so strong because you come to me with a sword, spear, and javelin. I come to you in the name of the Lord Almighty, the God of the armies of Israel, whom you mock. God will hand you over to me today. I will strike you down and cut off your head. The birds and beasts will be eating your flesh, not mine. Everyone here will know that it is not by the sword or spear that God saves. The battle is the Lord's, and he will give all of you into our hands.
Narrator 3:	Goliath moved closer to David and prepared to end the fight quickly.
Narrator 1:	David swiftly moved to the battle line to meet his enemy.
Narrator 2:	David reached into his bag and took out one stone.
Narrator 3:	He placed it in his sling, whirled the sling over his head, and let go.
Narrator 1:	The stone traveled about 80 miles an hour, and it hit Goliath in the head.
Narrator 2:	Goliath didn't even have time to blink as he fell facedown on the ground.
Narrator 1:	David ran to the giant, stood over him, and used Goliath's own sword to cut off his head.
Narrator 2:	When the Philistines saw that their champion was dead, they turned and ran.
Narrator 3:	The Israelite soldiers ran forward, shouting, and chased the Philistines.
Narrator 1:	God granted the army of Israel a great victory that day.

David and Goliath

Name ______________________________

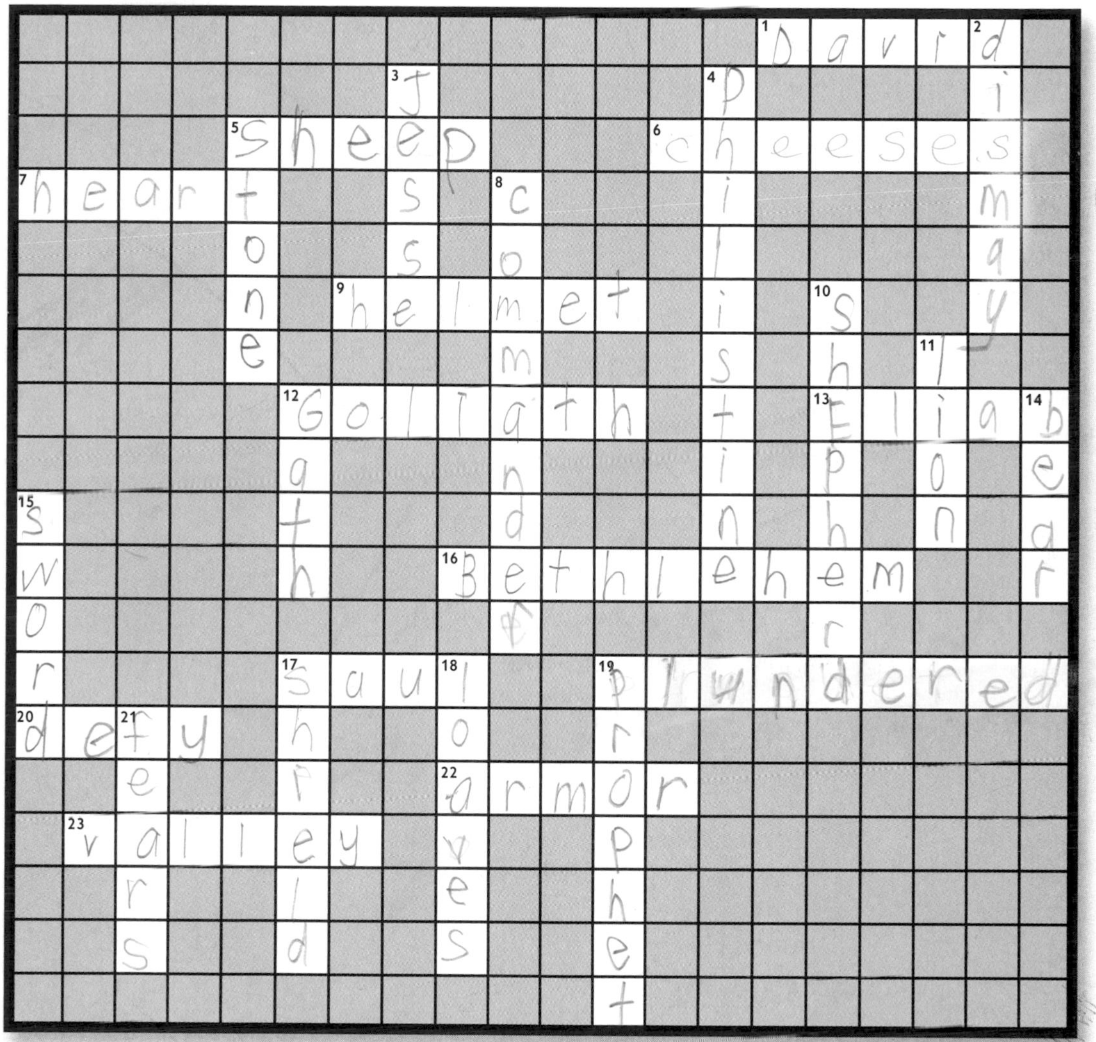

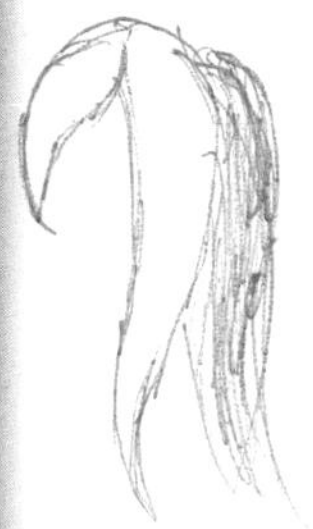

Across

1. _________ answered, "I am the son of your servant Jesse."
5. David told Saul he had protected his father's _________.
6. Jesse sent ten _________ to the commander of his sons' unit.
7. Man looks at the outward appearance, but God looks at the _________.
9. Goliath wore a bronze _________ on his head.
12. David came against _________ in the name of the Lord.
13. _________ burned with anger.
16. David was from _________.
17. _________ asked, "Whose son is that young man?"
19. The Israelites returned from the Philistine camp after having _______ their camp.
20. Who is he that he should _________ the armies of the living God?
22. David could barely walk while wearing Saul's _________.
23. Between the two hills was a _________.

Down

2. On hearing Goliath's words, the Israelites were filled with _________ and terror.
3. _________ sent gifts of bread and cheese.
4. Goliath was not an Israelite but a _________.
5. David reached into his bag and took out a _________.
8. Jesse sent ten loaves as a gift for the _________ of their unit.
10. In God's name, a _________ boy had defeated a Philistine champion.
11. David told how he had killed a _________ and a bear.
12. Goliath was from the town of _________.
14. Your servant has killed both the lion and the _________.
15. It is not by _________ or spear that the Lord saves.
17. His _________ bearer went ahead of him.
18. David brought his brothers ten _________ of bread.
19. David had been anointed by the _________ Samuel.
21. The Israelites had many _________ when they saw Goliath.

Saul's Jealousy

Name _____6/1/18_____ #6

Look up these Bible references from the Book of 1 Samuel and complete the following sentences.

1. **18:6–9** Saul became jealous of David because _the women sang that Saul has killed thousands, but David has killed tens of thousands._

2. **18:10–11** Saul tried to kill David by _trying to pin David to the wall while he was playing the lyre._

3. **18:12** Saul was afraid of David because _the Lord was with David and left Saul._

4. **18:24–25** Before he could marry Saul's daughter Michal, David had to _kill the Philistines and bring 100 foreskins back._

5. **18:25** Saul's plan was to have the Philistines _____
   _____

6. **18:28** Saul's attempts to kill David failed because _____
   _____

7. **19:10** Saul again tried to kill David by _____
   _____

8. **19:12–14** Michal helped David escape by _____
   _____

9. **19:23–24** When Saul followed David to Naioth, _____
   _____

Forever Friends

Write down as many characteristics of friends as you can in three minutes. If you could create the perfect friend, what would he or she be like?

_____

_____

_____

A Friend Is Like . . .

A simile is a comparison of one object or idea with another object or idea, using the words *like* or *as*. Write three similes that compare friendship with something else, and write how David and Jonathan's friendship reflects your simile. For example, you could say that a friend is like a diary because she knows your secrets but never tells. Jonathan knew where David was, but he didn't tell Saul.

1. A friend is like _____

   because _____

   In David and Jonathan's case, _____

   _____

2. A friend is like _____

   because _____

   In David and Jonathan's case, _____

   _____

3. A friend is like _____

   because _____

   In David and Jonathan's case, _____

   _____

Guided by God

Use the following instructions and questions as a guide as you read 1 Samuel 23–24.

David and the People of Keilah—1 Samuel 23:1–13

1. List the three times in these verses that David asked God what he should do.

   _____

   _____

   _____

   _____

David and Jonathan—1 Samuel 23:14–18

2. What did Jonathan tell David when they met in the Desert of Ziph? _____

   _____

   _____

God Provides for David—1 Samuel 23:19–29

3. How did God provide for David as Saul chased him in the desert? Why did Saul and his men

   suddenly leave? _____

   _____

   _____

David Spares Saul—1 Samuel 24

4. Who was looking for David in the Desert of En Gedi? _____

   _____

5. What did David do rather than kill Saul when he had the opportunity? _____

   _____

6. Why did David feel guilty about what he had done? _____

   _____

7. What does this tell you about David? _____

   _____

8. How did Saul respond after David told him how he had spared Saul's life? _____

_____

9. What was David's oath to Saul? _____

_____

10. Do you think that Saul would continue to be sorry for trying to kill David? Why or why not?

_____

_____

_____

_____

David Spares Saul Again—1 Samuel 26

11. Why wouldn't David allow Saul to be killed? _____

_____

12. How was God training David to be Israel's next king during his time on the run? _____

_____

_____

_____

_____

David, Nabal, and Abigail

Name _____

Read 1 Samuel 25: Follow the instructions and answer the questions.

1. Describe Nabal. _____

2. Describe Abigail. _____

3. What message did David send to Nabal? _____
_____

4. What was Nabal's response? _____
_____

5. What did David threaten to do? _____
_____

6. How did Nabal's wife, Abigail, respond? _____
_____
_____

7. What happened to Nabal? _____
_____
_____

8. How did David react to Nabal's death? _____
_____

9. Why did David take another wife? _____
_____
_____
_____

10. How does this story illustrate the words of Proverbs 15:1? _____
_____
_____
_____

Saul and the Witch of Endor

Name _____

Mark whether each statement is true (T) or false (F) according to 1 Samuel 28. Correct the false statements.

____ 1. Magic was legal in Israel.

_____

____ 2. Saul was afraid because David had threatened him.

_____

____ 3. Saul called on God, but God did not answer him.

_____

____ 4. Saul went to see the witch of Endor.

_____

____ 5. Saul put on other clothes and went at night because this was the custom.

_____

____ 6. The witch mocked Saul.

_____

____ 7. Saul learned that David was finally going to kill him.

_____

____ 8. Saul learned that he would win the battle.

_____

David and the Amalekites

After reading 1 Samuel 30, choose the correct word from the plunder below to complete each sentence. Some words may be used more than once.

1. _____ burned Ziklag and took all of the women and children with them.

2. _____ talked about stoning David.

3. _____ asked the Lord, "Shall I chase the Amalekites?"

4. _____ told David, "Chase them. You will be able to rescue the women and children."

5. Because they were too tired to go along, _____ stayed behind.

6. _____ led David and his men to the Amalekites.

7. _____ fought the Amalekites and took back the captives and their possessions.

8. _____ did not want to share the plunder with the men who stayed behind.

9. _____ said, "All will share alike."

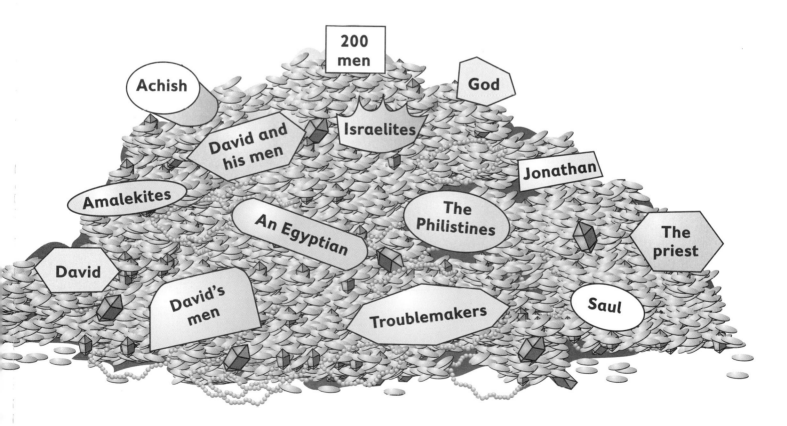

The Deaths of Jonathan and Saul

Name _____

After reading 1 Samuel 31 and 2 Samuel 1, choose the correct word from the weapons below to complete each sentence.

1. Now the _____ fought against Israel.

2. They killed Saul's sons, _____, Abinadab, and Malki-Shua.

3. _____ wounded Saul critically.

4. Saul wanted his _____ to kill him.

5. He wouldn't do it, but, like Saul, fell on his own _____.

6. The Philistines dishonored Saul and his sons. They put their _____ in the _____ of the Ashtoreths and fastened their bodies to the _____ of Beth Shan.

7. Valiant men from _____ removed the bodies and buried them.

8. An _____ who told David of Saul's death was trying to take credit for killing him but instead was put to death.

9. David and his men _____ and wept and fasted for Saul and Jonathan.

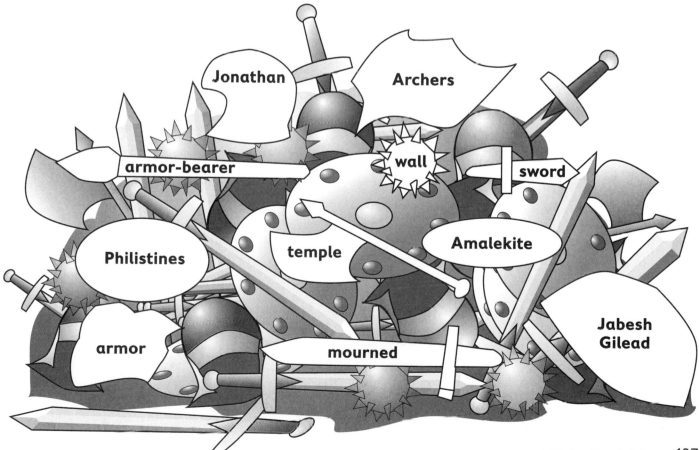

David Becomes King

Name _____

David did not become king over all of Israel right away. The following Bible verses from 2 Samuel tell about events that made David's kingdom stronger. Read each Bible passage, and describe the event in one sentence. The first one has been done for you.

1. **2:4** <u>David was anointed king over Judah</u>
   <u>at Hebron.</u>

2. **2:12–17** _____
   _____

3. **3:1–5** _____
   _____
   _____

4. **3:17–21** _____
   _____
   _____

5. **4:5–6** _____
   _____

6. **5:1–3** _____
   _____

7. **5:6–7** _____
   _____

8. **5:9** _____
   _____

9. **5:17–20** _____
   _____

10. **5:22–25** _____
    _____

David Begins His Reign

Compare and contrast the way David first tried to bring the ark into Jerusalem with the way he finally brought the ark there according to to 2 Samuel 6.

	First time	Second time
People		
Transportation for the ark		
Actions by David and the people		
The ark's new home		
Celebration for the ark's return		
Blessings		

1. Why did Michal disapprove of David's joyful dance? _____

_____

2. What was David's reply to his wife? _____

_____

3. Why did David bring the ark back to Jerusalem? _____

_____

_____

4. How can we avoid the mistake David made? _____

_____

_____

Psalm 24

First, write as much of Psalm 24 as you can without using the code. Then use the code to fill in the rest.

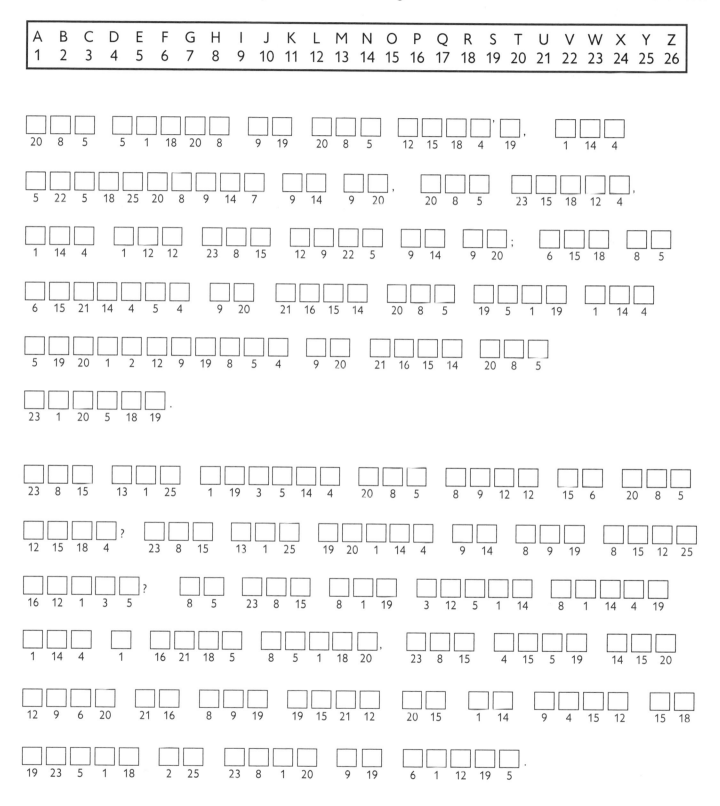

A	B	C	D	E	F	G	H	I	J	K	L	M	N	O	P	Q	R	S	T	U	V	W	X	Y	Z
1	2	3	4	5	6	7	8	9	10	11	12	13	14	15	16	17	18	19	20	21	22	23	24	25	26

HE WILL RECEIVE BLESSING FROM

THE LORD AND VINDICATION FROM

GOD HIS SAVIOR. SUCH IS THE

GENERATION OF THOSE WHO SEEK

HIM, WHO SEEK YOUR FACE, O GOD

OF JACOB.

LIFT UP YOUR HEADS, O YOU

GATES; BE LIFTED UP, YOU

ANCIENT DOORS, THAT THE KING

OF GLORY MAY COME IN. WHO IS

THIS KING OF GLORY? THE LORD

STRONG AND MIGHTY, THE LORD

MIGHTY IN BATTLE. LIFT UP

YOUR HEADS, O YOU GATES;

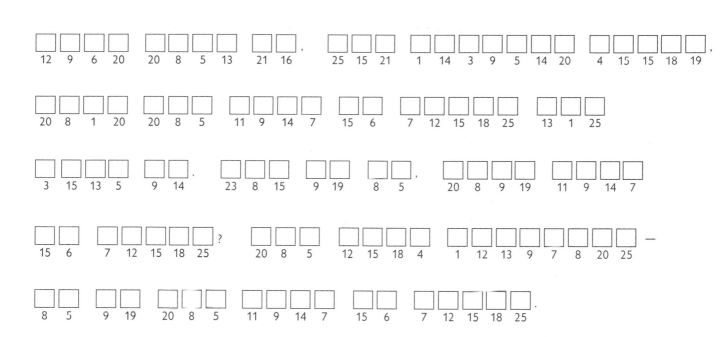

12 9 6 20 20 8 5 13 21 16 , 25 15 21 1 14 3 9 5 14 20 4 15 15 18 19 ,

20 8 1 20 20 8 5 11 9 14 7 15 6 7 12 15 18 25 13 1 25

3 15 13 5 9 14 . 23 8 15 9 19 8 5 , 20 8 9 19 11 9 14 7

15 6 7 12 15 18 25 ? 20 8 5 12 15 18 4 1 12 13 9 7 8 20 25 —

8 5 9 19 20 8 5 11 9 14 7 15 6 7 12 15 18 25 .

David's Sin

Write down the Ten Commandments. (Look at Exodus 20:1–17 or Deuteronomy 5:7–21 if you need help remembering them.) Put an asterisk (*) in front of the commandments that David broke, and tell how he broke them.

Read Leviticus 20:10. What was the penalty for David and Bathsheba's sin supposed to be?

_____

Trouble in David's Family

Name _____

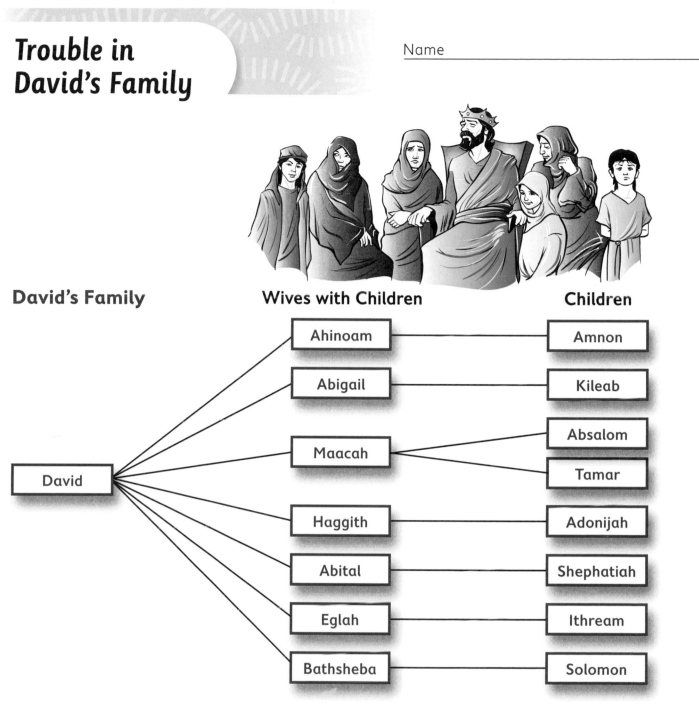

David's Family   **Wives with Children**   **Children**

David

- Ahinoam — Amnon
- Abigail — Kileab
- Maacah — Absalom / Tamar
- Haggith — Adonijah
- Abital — Shephatiah
- Eglah — Ithream
- Bathsheba — Solomon

Outline of 2 Samuel 13–19

1. Amnon and Tamar—2 Samuel 13:1–22

   a. _____

   _____

   b. _____

2. Absalom Gets Revenge—2 Samuel 13:23–38

   a. _____

   b. _____

3. Absalom Returns—2 Samuel 14:1–33

   a. _____

   b. _____

   c. _____

   d. _____

4. Absalom Plots to Take the Kingdom—2 Samuel 15:1–12

   a. _____

   b. _____

   c. _____

   d. _____

5. David Flees Jerusalem—2 Samuel 15:13–37

   a. _____

   _____

   b. _____

6. David on the Run—2 Samuel 16:1–14

   a. _____

   _____

   b. _____

7. Hushai and Ahithophel Give Advice—2 Samuel 16:15—17:14

   a. _____

   _____

   b. _____

   _____

8. A Message Is Sent to David—2 Samuel 17:15–29

   a. _____

   b. _____

   c. _____

9. Absalom's Death—2 Samuel 18:1–18

   a. _____

   b. _____

   c. _____

   d. _____

10. David Mourns Absalom—2 Samuel 18:19—19:8

   a. _____

   b. _____

      _____

   c. _____

11. The Road to Jerusalem—2 Samuel 19:9–43

   a. _____

   b. _____

   c. _____

   d. _____

   e. _____

      _____

David's Last Years

Use 1 Kings 1 to fill in the blanks. When you are finished, read the summary of this story.

David's son, _____, decided that he wanted to be _____.

_____ and _____ supported him. When _____ found out

about this, he advised _____ to speak to _____ about his promise to make

her son, _____, king. She went to David in his _____ and told him what had

happened. Then Nathan the _____ arrived and told David that Adonijah had invited all

the _____ _____, the _____ _____ of the _____, and Abiathar

the _____ to a feast. Nathan said "Right now they are eating and drinking with him

and saying "'_____ _____ _____ _____.'"

David promised that _____ would be king. He ordered _____,

_____, and _____ to come to him. Then he told them to take

_____ to _____ on his _____ and to _____

him king over Israel. Then they should blow the _____ and shout "_____ _____

_____ _____." The three men did as David had told them. When the people celebrating

with _____ heard what had happened, they were afraid and ran away.

Who's Who and What's What?

Name _____

Write the name of the character or object described.

1. I was the son of King Saul who became king over 10 tribes after my father's death. _____

2. I really made all the decisions for Ish-Bosheth. _____

3. I decided to go to David's side and try to rally Israel to make him king. _____

4. I killed Abner before he could carry out his plan. _____

5. David was first anointed king over Israel here. _____

6. David then captured the fortress of Zion, now known as this city. _____

7. The ark was first moved on this, pulled by oxen. _____

8. I touched the ark and died. _____

9. Only this group of people was allowed to move the ark. _____

10. I was blessed while the ark was left at my home. _____

11. I led great rejoicing as the ark was returned to Jerusalem. _____

12. I was very embarrassed at my husband's dance. _____

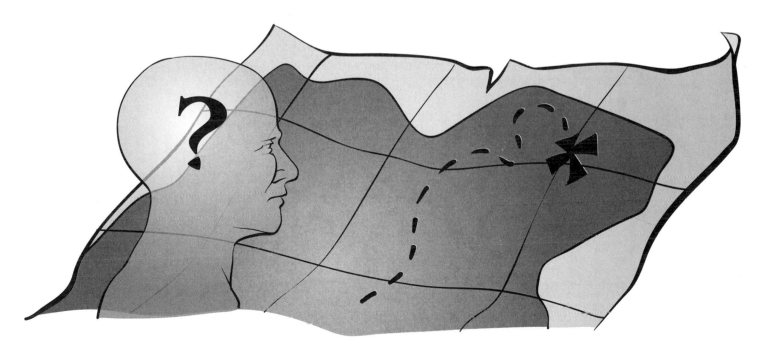

13. David wanted to build this as a fitting home for God. _____

14. I was lame because of an accident in which my nurse dropped me when I was just five years old. _____

15. I was the servant who told King David about Jonathan's son. _____

16. I was the wife of Uriah. _____

17. I did not lead my men out to battle and was faced with temptation. _____

18. I confronted David about his sin. _____

19. David heard a story about this animal from the prophet. _____

20. David repented and asked God's forgiveness for this. _____

21. I was a handsome man with beautiful, long hair. _____

22. Absalom arranged for the murder of this half-brother who had disgraced Tamar.

_____

23. I did not discipline my children properly. _____

24. I tried to make Israel think that I would be a better king than my father, David.

_____

25. I did not bring Mephibosheth the donkey as I had promised. _____

26. I acted as a spy for David and gave Absalom bad advice. _____

27. I killed myself because David did not listen to my advice. _____

28. I was another son of David who thought I should be the next king. _____

29. My mother was Bathsheba. _____

30. God made one of these with David, promising that he would establish David's throne forever.

_____

Solomon Chooses Wisdom

Name _____

Answer the following questions with your class as you read the Scripture passages.

1 Kings 3:1–15

1. Why did Solomon marry Pharaoh's daughter? _____

   _____

   _____

   _____

2. How did Solomon show his love for God? _____

   _____

   _____

3. What sin did Solomon and the people commit? _____

   _____

   _____

4. What was their excuse for their sin? _____

5. What did God offer Solomon? _____

6. What did Solomon choose? Why? _____

   _____

7. What did God tell Solomon that he would also give him? _____

   _____

   _____

   _____

1 Kings 3:16–28

8. What did both of the women claim?_____

9. How did Solomon discover the identity of the true mother?_____

   _____

1 Kings 4:29–34

10. What does 1 Kings 4 say about Solomon's wisdom? _____

_____

_____

11. What did Solomon write and teach about? _____

_____

12. Who knew about Solomon's wisdom? _____

_____

2 Chronicles 1:14–17

13. God promised Solomon that he would also give him

    wealth. What examples of his wealth do you see in this

    passage?_____

_____

_____

_____

Think about It

14. How do you think Solomon could have used his wisdom to be a blessing to God's people? ____

_____

_____

_____

15. How do you think Solomon could have used his wealth to be a blessing to God's people? ____

_____

_____

_____

Solomon's Temple

Name _____

Look up the passages in the Book of 1 Kings, and fill in the blanks.

The Workers. Many people helped build the temple: _____ laborers from Israel

(5:13), _____ carriers and _____ stonecutters from the

peoples conquered by the Israelites (5:15), and _____ foremen

or supervisors (5:16).

The Materials. Solomon traded _____

and _____ with Hiram, king of

Tyre, for the _____ and

_____ needed to build the temple

(5:10–11). The foundation for the temple was

made of _____ (5:17).

The Holy Place. The inside walls of the temple were made of _____ wood and the

floors were made of _____ (6:15). There was also a golden _____,

a golden _____ for the bread of the Presence, and ten golden _____

(7:48–49).

The Most Holy Place. The inside of the Most Holy Place was covered with _____

(6:20). This room contained two large _____ (6:23) and the _____

of the covenant (8:6). Two _____ spread their wings over the _____

(8:7). The Most Holy Place also contained the _____ that Moses had received

from God at Mount Sinai (8:9).

The Building. The outside of the temple was made of _____ taken from the quarries

(6:7). There were ten bronze _____ (7:27) with ten bronze _____

(7:38) that were used to wash animal sacrifices. In the courtyard outside the temple was a large

altar used for burnt offerings, and there was also a bronze _____ (7:23) that was

used by the priests for washing.

Fill in the names of the parts of the temple building shown here.

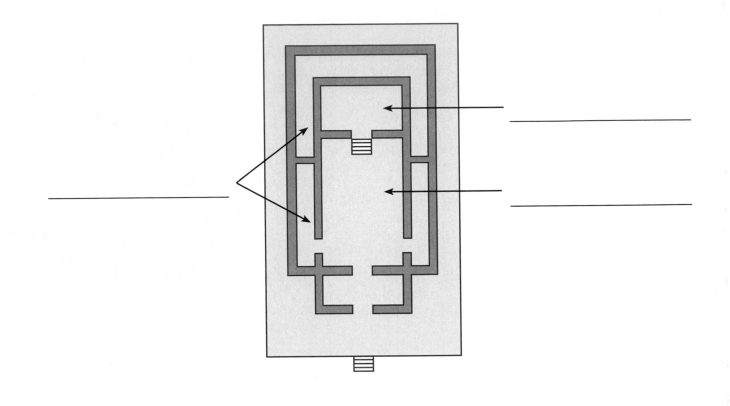

Solomon's Kingdom

Name _____

Use the Bible and Bible resources to find out about Solomon's kingdom.

1. The queen of Sheba gave Solomon 120 talents of gold.

   How much gold was that? _____

   _____

   Where did you find this information? _____

   _____

   _____

   _____

2. Find a picture of the ruins of what might have been Solomon's stable. Where do some people

   think it is? _____

   Where did you find this information? _____

   _____

3. Who were the laborers for Solomon's projects? _____

   _____

   Where did you find this information? _____ _____

4. Find out what Solomon's ships may have been like. _____

   _____

   Where did you find this information? _____

   _____

5. Where did Solomon's ships sail? _____

   Where did you find this information? _____

   _____

6. Solomon had a fleet of his own trading ships, along with the ships of Hiram. What did these

   ships bring back? _____

   Where did you find this information? _____

   _____

7. Draw a picture of Solomon's throne below or on another piece of paper.

   Where did you find this information? _____

   _____

8. What kinds of gifts did Solomon receive from the queen of Sheba? _____

   _____

   Where did you find this information? _____

   _____

Wealth and Money

Name _____

Fill in the blanks to find out what the Bible says about wealth and money.

1. "But remember the _____ your _____, for it is _____ who gives you the _____ to produce _____" (Deuteronomy 8:18).

2. "But man, despite his _____, does not endure; he is like the _____ that perish" (Psalm 49:12).

3. "_____ the _____ with your _____" (Proverbs 3:9).

4. "_____ is _____ in the day of _____, but _____ delivers from _____" (Proverbs 11:4).

5. "Whoever trusts in his _____ will _____, but the righteous will thrive like a _____ _____" (Proverbs 11:28).

6. "Better a _____ with the _____ of the _____ than great _____ with turmoil" (Proverbs 15:16).

7. "A good _____ is more desirable than great _____; to be esteemed is better than _____ or _____" (Proverbs 22:1).

8. "Whoever loves _____ never has _____ enough; whoever loves _____ is never _____ with his income" (Ecclesiastes 5:10).

9. "You cannot serve both _____ and _____" (Matthew 6:24b).

10. "For the love of _____ is a root of all kinds of _____" (1 Timothy 6:10).

11. "Command those who are _____ in this present _____ not to be _____ nor to put their _____ in _____, which is so _____, but to put their hope in _____, who richly provides us with _____ for our _____" (1 Timothy 6:17).

Solomon's Bad Choices

Name _____

Use the clues on the following page, along with 1 Kings 11, to fill in the answers to the puzzle. The box will give you the theme of this lesson.

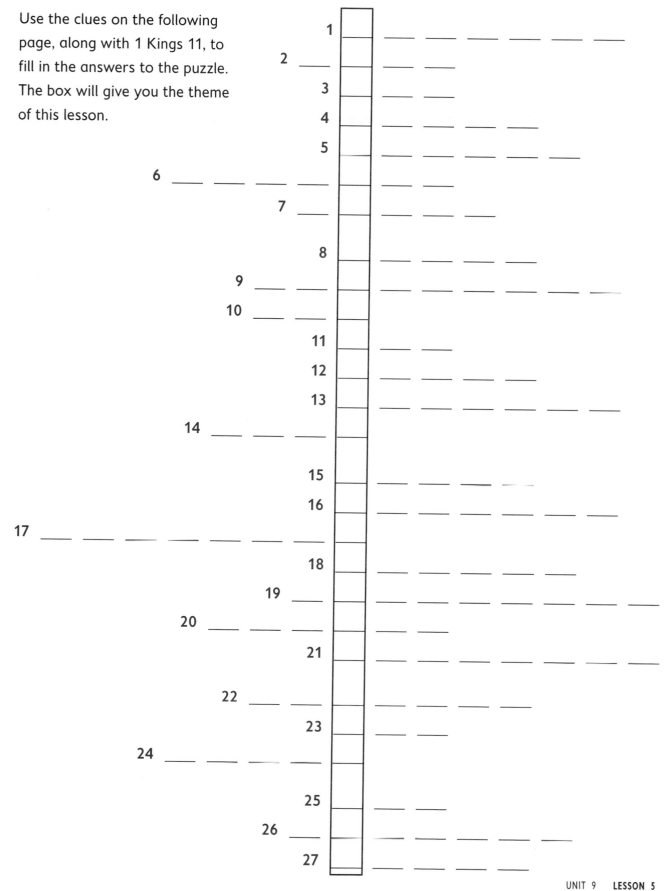

1. King _____ loved many foreign women.

2. The _____ told the Israelites not to marry people from other nations.

3. Solomon's wives _____ him astray.

4. Solomon's heart turned to _____ gods.

5. He followed the gods Ashtoreth and _____.

6. Solomon built a high place for _____.

7. God became _____ with Solomon.

8. God appeared to Solomon _____.

9. God had _____ Solomon not to follow other gods.

10. God told Solomon, "I will tear the kingdom away from _____."

11. The kingdom would be torn out of the hand of Solomon's _____.

12. God would give him one _____ for the sake of David.

13. The Lord raised up Hadad the _____ against Solomon.

14. Hadad had _____ to Egypt as a boy.

15. _____ wanted to return to his own country.

16. Rezon was also _____ enemy while Solomon lived.

17. _____, son of Nebat, rebelled against Solomon.

18. Ahijah was the prophet of _____.

19. He met Jeroboam as he was leaving _____.

20. Ahijah tore his cloak into _____ pieces.

21. Solomon had _____ God.

22. God would not take the whole _____ away from Solomon.

23. God would give _____ tribe to Solomon's son.

24. If Jeroboam did what was _____, God would be with him.

25. _____ humbled David's descendants.

26. _____ tried to kill Jeroboam.

27. Solomon was buried in the city of _____.

The Psalms

Psalms are prayers and songs that are expressed through poetry. As we learn to understand and appreciate them, they can help us express our thoughts and feelings to God and to grow closer to him.

1. What kind of poem or poetic device is used in the following psalms?

   a. Psalm 125:1 _____

   b. Psalm 98:8 _____

   c. Psalm 40:4 _____

   d. Psalm 119 _____

   e. Psalm 136 _____

   f. Psalm 119:105 _____

A simile is a comparison using *like* or *as.*

An acrostic begins each line or section with a certain letter.

A metaphor is a comparison that does not use *like* or *as.*

Parallelism develops the thought further in its second line.

Repetition repeats a thought for emphasis.

Personification gives human traits to objects.

2. Write your own psalm expressing your thoughts or feelings to God.

   Try to use at least one poetic device in your psalm.

   _____

   _____

   _____

   _____

   _____

   _____

   _____

Kinds of Psalms

There are many ways to classify the psalms. Some of these classifications are:

HISTORY

TRUST

MESSIANIC

CURSING

CONFESSION

PRAISE

Name _____

Read the following verses and use the words in the box to classify each type of psalm. On the lines that follow, write one phrase or sentence from each reference that represents that type of psalm.

1. Psalm 2:4–9 _____

2. Psalm 16:1–3 _____

3. Psalm 51:9–12 _____

4. Psalm 66:1–3 _____

5. Psalm 109:6–9 _____

6. Psalm 135:8–12 _____

Psalm _____

Answer the following questions about the psalm that you have been assigned.

1. What type of psalm is it? _____

2. What is a key verse of the psalm? _____

3. What can you learn from this psalm? _____

_____

_____

_____

Use your creativity to illustrate this psalm.

Psalms of David

Look up the following Bible references. Write down the situation that David was in when he wrote the psalm. Read the passage. In the space provided, note what can be learned from that passage.

Reference	Situation	Application
Psalm 3		
Psalm 18 (Read verses 30–36, 46.)		
Psalm 34 (Read verses 1–3, 17–21.)		
Psalm 51 (Read verses 1–4, 7–12.)		
Psalm 57		

God is Like . . .

Name _____

In Psalm 23 David describes God as a shepherd caring for his sheep. He is David's fortress and shield in Psalm 18. Think of some other examples of similes and metaphors to describe God. Write and illustrate them below.

The Lord is like Superman watching over the city of Metropolis.

The Lord takes care of me the way the water and I take care of my fish.

Meeting God and Yourself in the Psalms

Name _____

1. Many of the psalms teach us about the character of God.

   Read the following examples, and write what that passage teaches us about God.

   a. Psalm 19:1–3 _____

   b. Psalm 71:5–8 _____

   c. Psalm 115:1–8 _____

   d. Psalm 115:9–11 _____

   e. Psalm 136 _____

   f. Psalm 139:1–4 _____

   g. Psalm 139:7–12 _____

   h. Psalm 139:13–18 _____

   i. Psalm 145:1–3 _____

   j. Psalm 145:4–6 _____

   k. Psalm 145:14–16 _____

2. The psalms can also teach us about ourselves.

   Fill in the blanks describing what can be learned from the following passages.

   a. Psalm 8:5—God gives me a place of _____ in creation.

   b. Psalm 9:1–2—God desires my _____.

   c. Psalm 13—I can be _____ with God about
   my feelings.

   d. Psalm 14:3—I am not _____ apart from God.

   e. Psalm 19:7–8—I need to make God's _____
   a priority.

   f. Psalm 27:1–3—Despite troubles around me, I can be
   _____.

   g. Psalm 32:1–2—I can be _____.

   h. Psalm 46:10—I need to take time to be _____ before God.

Themes in the Book of Proverbs

Name _____

Read the Scripture passages from each of the 8 boxes below. Each box of passages is focused around a certain theme. See if you can figure out what each theme is. Hint, the number of letters in the word equals the number of spaces below each box. When you have filled in the answers correctly, you will discover something about the book of Proverbs.

7

10:4
12:11
13:4
18:9
20:13

2

10:19
12:6
14:25
25:11
28:23

6

17:17
18:24
19:4
19:6
27:6

1

1:8
10:1
13:24
20:7
23:24

3

10:22
16:8
16:16
22:1
22:2

4

1:7
2:6
3:13
4:7
13:14

5

14:17
15:18
16:32
19:19
29:22

8

11:25
14:21
14:31
19:17
21:13

and
the

___

___

___

and

___

___ b ___ o k ___ f ___ i s ___ ___ a y ___ n ___ s

___

___

___

___

Poetry in the Proverbs

Name _____

1. Name the poetic device used in the following proverbs:

   a. "Wisdom calls aloud in the street, she raises her voice in the public squares; at the head of the noisy streets she cries out, in the gateways of the city she makes her speech" (Proverbs 1:20–21). _____

   b. "Pride goes before destruction, a haughty spirit before a fall" (Proverbs 16:18). _____

   c. "Wine is a mocker and beer a brawler; whoever is led astray by them is not wise" (Proverbs 20:1). _____

   d. "The king's heart is in the hand of the Lord; he directs it like a watercourse wherever he pleases" (Proverbs 21:1). _____

2. Various types of parallelism are used in the Book of Proverbs. One common kind is the contrast of opposites. Read the following proverbs, and tell who or what is being contrasted.

   a. "Blessings crown the head of the righteous, but violence overwhelms the mouth of the wicked" (Proverbs 10:6). _____

   b. "The wise in heart accept commands, but a chattering fool comes to ruin" (Proverbs 10:8).

   _____

   c. "A wife of noble character is her husband's crown, but a disgraceful wife is like decay in his bones" (Proverbs 12:4). _____

   d. "A gentle answer turns away wrath, but a harsh word stirs up anger" (Proverbs 15:1).

   _____

   e. "A happy heart makes the face cheerful, but heartache crushes the spirit" (Proverbs 15:13). _____

   f. "Understanding is a fountain of life to those who have it, but folly brings punishment to fools" (Proverbs 16:22). _____

   g. "He who works his land will have abundant food, but the one who chases fantasies will have his fill of poverty" (Proverbs 28:19). _____

Proverbs: Sayings of the Wise

Name _____

Fill in the blank by using the corresponding verse from the Book of Proverbs.

1. "The fear of the LORD is the beginning of ⬚⬚⬚⬚⬚⬚⬚⬚" (1:7).
   (33 17   44)

2. "My son, if ⬚⬚⬚⬚⬚⬚ entice you, do not give in to them" (1:10).
   (9   37)

3. "Let love and ⬚⬚⬚⬚⬚⬚⬚⬚⬚⬚⬚⬚ never leave you; bind them
   (4   38   2)

   around your neck, write them on the tablet of your heart" (3:3).

4. "In all your ways ⬚⬚⬚⬚⬚⬚⬚⬚⬚⬚ him, and he will make your paths
   (1   27)

   straight" (3:6).

5. "Go to the ant, you ⬚⬚⬚⬚⬚⬚⬚; consider its ways and be wise!" (6:6).
   (10   26)

6. "Lazy hands make a man poor, but ⬚⬚⬚⬚⬚⬚⬚ hands bring wealth" (10:4).
   (40 14)

7. "A ⬚⬚⬚⬚⬚ betrays a confidence, but a trustworthy man keeps a secret" (11:13).
   (6)

8. "Reckless words pierce like a ⬚⬚⬚⬚, but the tongue of the wise brings
   (12 41)

   healing" (12:18).

9. "He who walks with the wise grows wise, but a ⬚⬚⬚⬚⬚⬚⬚ of fools
   (22 18   39 43 42)

   suffers harm" (13:20).

10. "He who ignores ⬚⬚⬚⬚⬚⬚⬚⬚⬚ despises himself, but whoever heeds
    (19)

    correction gains understanding" (15:32).

11. "⬚⬚⬚⬚⬚ goes before destruction, a haughty spirit before a fall" (16:18).
    (3 28)

12. "The crucible for silver and the furnace for gold, but the LORD tests the

▢▢▢▢▢" (17:3).
　15　35　29

13. "Starting a ▢▢▢▢▢▢▢ is like breaching a dam; so drop the matter before
　　　　　　　　　24

a dispute breaks out" (17:14).

14. "A cheerful heart is good ▢▢▢▢▢▢▢, but a crushed spirit dries up the
　　　　　　　　　25　31　　16　　21

bones" (17:22).

15. "The name of the LORD is a strong ▢▢▢▢▢; the righteous run to it and
　　　　　　　　　　　　　23　　5

are safe" (18:10).

16. "A good ▢▢▢▢ is more desirable than great riches" (22:1).
　　　　30　11

17. "Train a ▢▢▢▢▢ in the way he should go, and when he is old he will not turn
　　　　8　　34

from it" (22:6).

18. "Better is open ▢▢▢▢▢▢ than hidden love" (27:5).
　　　　　36　　32　20

19. "As iron sharpens iron, so one ▢▢▢ sharpens another" (27:17).
　　　　　　　　　　7

20. "Charm is deceptive, and ▢▢▢▢▢▢ is fleeting; but a woman who fears the
　　　　　　　　　　13

LORD is to be praised" (31:30).

"For the LORD gives wisdom,

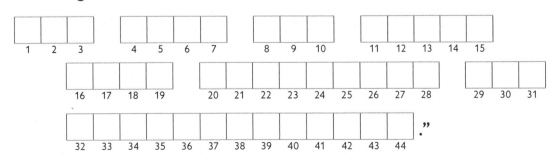

▢▢▢　▢▢▢▢　▢▢▢　▢▢▢▢▢
1　2　3　4　5　6　7　8　9　10　11　12　13　14　15

▢▢▢▢　▢▢▢▢▢▢▢▢▢　▢▢▢
16　17　18　19　20　21　22　23　24　25　26　27　28　29　30　31

▢▢▢▢▢▢▢▢▢▢▢▢▢."
32　33　34　35　36　37　38　39　40　41　42　43　44

Extra: Do you know where this passage is found in Proverbs? _____

174

Word Pictures in Proverbs

Word pictures are a literary device that aids in the understanding of a truth. The Book of Proverbs contains many word pictures, each explaining some nugget of truth. Examples of word pictures are found in 3:7–8; 4:7–9; 6:6, 23; 8:11; 9:9; 10:4, 5, 25; 11:13, 22, 30; 12:10, 18; 15:1, 6, 17; 16:16; 17:6, 12, 22; 18:10; 19:12, 23; 20:4, 15, 29; 21:19; 22:1; 23:31–32; 25:11, 20, 24; 26:20; 27:17, 19; 30:5. Choose one word picture from the above verses or from another verse in the Book of Proverbs to illustrate below. Write the reference and verse below your picture.

_____

_____

_____

_____

The Divided Kingdom

Name _____

Use the map of the divided kingdom to answer the following questions.

1. Was Jerusalem located in Judah or Israel? _____

2. What was the city farthest south that was ever part of Judah?

   _____

3. What river flowed through Israel?

   _____

4. What city located on Judah's northern border was almost in Israel?

   _____

5. Name one of the cities in the far north that was part of Israel.

   _____

6. What sea is located west of the divided kingdom? _____

7. What group of people occupied the land west of Judah? _____

8. What group of people occupied the land west of Israel? _____

9. Label Jericho and Damascus on the map.

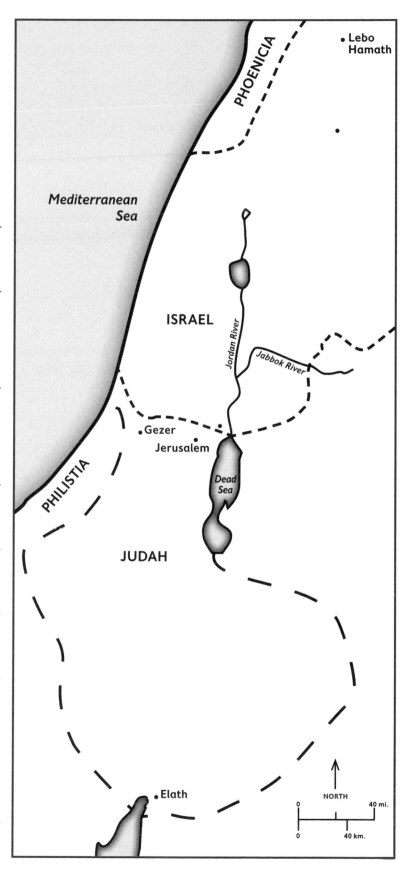

Jeroboam's Golden Calves

Name _____

The Golden Calves

1. Who had made a golden calf long before Jeroboam did? _____

2. What happened to that golden calf? _____

   _____

3. Why did Jeroboam make the golden calves? _____

   _____

   _____

   _____

4. Why did Jeroboam choose a calf? _____

   _____

5. Why did Jeroboam put the calves at Dan and Bethel? _____

   _____

   _____

6. Name two other things Jeroboam did that were wrong. _____

   _____

7. What two miracles happened when Jeroboam tried to seize the man of God? _____

   _____

A Visit to Ahijah

8. Why did Jeroboam's wife go to Ahijah? _____

   _____

9. Why did she disguise herself? _____

   _____

10. What bad news did Ahijah give her? _____

    _____

    _____

Israel's Sins

God's Commands	Israel's Sins

Good King Asa

Look up the following verses in the Book of 2 Chronicles, and write down examples of good things that King Asa did during his reign over Judah.

1. **14:3–5** _____

   _____

2. **14:6–7** _____

   _____

3. **14:9–15** _____

   _____

4. **15:1–7** (Summarize the words of encouragement that Asa received from Azariah.) _____

   _____

   _____

5. **15:8** _____

   _____

6. **15:11–15** _____

   _____

7. **15:16** _____

   _____

8. **15:18** _____

   _____

Look up the following verses, and write down examples of bad things that Asa did during his reign over Judah.

9. 16:1–3 _____

_____

_____

10. 16:7–10 _____

_____

11. 16:12 _____

_____

For Better or Worse

Name _____

Influence is a powerful thing—it can be used for either good or evil. Look up the following verses and complete the chart below:

Scripture passage	Who was influenced?	Who was influencing?	Was the influence good or bad?
Genesis 3:4–6			
1 Thessalonians 1:6			
Exodus 32:1			
Titus 2:3–5			
Numbers 13:31—14:2			
2 Kings 23:3			
1 Kings 12:8–11			
1 Peter 5:1–3			
John 1:40–42			

1. Give three examples of how someone has influenced you. _____

_____

_____

_____

2. Give three examples of how you have been an influence on someone else. _____

_____

_____

_____

3. Think of something you could do this week to influence one person to grow closer to God.

Write it down. _____

_____

_____

4. Predict the results of King Ahab's listening to the negative influences around him and

becoming a poor influence on Israel. _____

_____

_____

_____

Five Kings

Name _____

Twenty-five facts about 5 kings are listed on this page and the next. Match each fact with the appropriate king by writing the fact number in the chart below. If you need help, look up the listed verses from 2 Chronicles 10–16 and 1 Kings 11–16.

1. He went to war against Jeroboam. (2 Chronicles 13:2–4)

2. He removed the foreign altars and got rid of the sacred stones and Asherah poles. (2 Chronicles 14:2–3)

3. He was given 10 pieces of robe by the prophet Ahijah. (1 Kings 11:31)

4. He fled to King Shishak of Egypt when Solomon tried to kill him. (1 Kings 11:40)

5. He built up the fortified cities of Judah during a time of peace. (2 Chronicles 14:6)

6. He had golden calves built for worship at Dan and Bethel. (1 Kings 12:28–30)

7. He rejected the advice of the elders concerning how to handle the people of Israel, so Israel rebelled against him. (2 Chronicles 10:13–19)

8. He called upon the Lord, and the Lord allowed Judah to be successful against the Cushites. (2 Chronicles 14:9–12)

9. He appointed non-Levite priests and created his own festivals. (1 Kings 12:31–32)

10. When he tried to seize the man of God, his hand shriveled and the altar split apart. (1 Kings 13:4–5)

Rehoboam	Abijah	Asa	Jeroboam	Ahab

Five Kings

11. He repaired the altar of the Lord and made sacrifices to God. (2 Chronicles 15:8–11)

12. His wife disguised herself and went to the prophet to see if their son would live. (1 Kings 14:1–4)

13. He pleaded with Jeroboam and the people of Israel not to resist the kingdom of the Lord. (2 Chronicles 13:4–12)

14. He planned to fight against Israel, but Shemaiah came to him with a message from God telling him not to fight. (2 Chronicles 11:2–4)

15. When he was attacked by Baasha, he sent gold to Ben-Hadad, king of Aram, so Ben–Hadad, attacked Israel instead. (2 Chronicles 16:1–4)

16. He began to serve and worship Baal. (1 Kings 16:31)

17. Hanani, a seer, came to him, telling him that he had not relied on the Lord. (2 Chronicles 16:7–9)

18. He defeated the Israelites because the people of Judah relied on God. (2 Chronicles 13:14–16)

19. He was the son of Omri and reigned 22 years. (1 Kings 16:29–30)

20. He did more to anger God than all the other kings of Israel before him. (1 Kings 16:33)

21. He was the first king of Judah. (2 Chronicles 12:1–4)

22. He ruled Judah for 17 years. (2 Chronicles 12:13)

23. He was influenced by his evil wife, Jezebel. (1 Kings 16:31)

24. He ruled over Judah for 3 years. (2 Chronicles 13:1–2)

25. He ruled over Judah for 41 years. (2 Chronicles 16:13)

Elijah

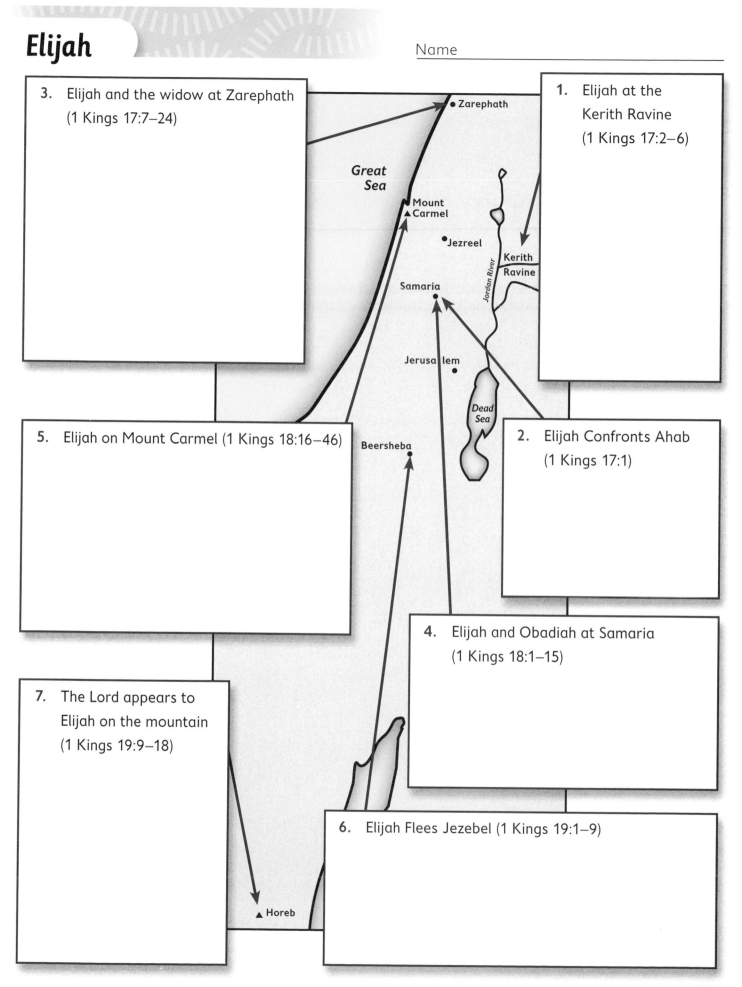

Name _____

3. Elijah and the widow at Zarephath (1 Kings 17:7–24)

1. Elijah at the Kerith Ravine (1 Kings 17:2–6)

Great Sea

Zarephath

Mount Carmel

Jezreel

Kerith Ravine

Jordan River

Samaria

Jerusalem

Dead Sea

5. Elijah on Mount Carmel (1 Kings 18:16–46)

Beersheba

2. Elijah Confronts Ahab (1 Kings 17:1)

4. Elijah and Obadiah at Samaria (1 Kings 18:1–15)

7. The Lord appears to Elijah on the mountain (1 Kings 19:9–18)

6. Elijah Flees Jezebel (1 Kings 19:1–9)

Horeb

Elijah's Contest

Narrator 1: After three years of famine, Elijah confronted King Ahab.

Narrator 2: Ahab was not happy to see God's prophet return.

Ahab: Is that you, you troublemaker of Israel?

Elijah: I haven't made trouble for Israel. If you want to see a troublemaker, look at yourself and at that evil woman you married. You have followed Baal instead of God. I challenge you and the priests of Baal to a competition. Bring the 450 prophets of Baal and the 400 prophets of Asherah to Mount Carmel. And gather the people of Israel at Mount Carmel, too. They need to see the contest between God's prophet and Baal's prophets.

Narrator 2: At the appointed time the people, the prophets of Baal and Asherah, and King Ahab gathered at Mount Carmel.

Narrator 3: Elijah shouted to the people of Israel.

Elijah: How long will you go back and forth serving God and then Baal? If the Lord is God, follow him—but if Baal is god, follow him.

Narrator 4: The people said nothing. They wanted to see what was going to happen next.

Elijah: I am the only one of the Lord's prophets left, but Baal has 450 prophets standing before you. Bring us two bulls. Baal's prophets can choose one and cut it into pieces. They should set it on their altar above the wood but not set fire to it. I will prepare the other bull in the same way. Then we will call on the name of the god we serve. The god who answers by fire—he is God.

People of Israel: So be it. What you say is good.

Elijah: Prophets of Baal, pick your bull and prepare it. Call on the name of your god, and we'll all see if he lights the altar on fire.

Narrator 5: The prophets of Baal began crying out to their god early in the morning.

Prophets of Baal: O Baal, answer us!

Narrator 3: By noon their voices were getting hoarse, but they kept shouting.

Prophets of Baal:	Baal, answer us! Send us fire!
Narrator 5:	Their god still didn't answer.
Narrator 4:	They begin dancing around the altar they had made to Baal, hoping to get their god's attention.
Prophets of Baal:	Baal, you see us serving you. Send us fire! Send us fire! Send us fire!
Elijah:	Maybe Baal is sleeping. I heard that he had a late night last night. Maybe if you yell a little louder, you can wake him up!
Prophets of Baal:	Baal, hear us. Do not let this prophet of God mock us!
Narrator 4:	The prophets of Baal shouted louder and louder. They even began to slash themselves with swords and spears.
Narrator 3:	Blood flowed from the wounds of Baal's prophets, but their god still gave them no answer.
Narrator 1:	The prophets became frantic. They yelled louder, cut themselves more deeply, and danced even more fiercely around their altar.
Narrator 2:	By late afternoon Baal's prophets had exhausted themselves. They lay at the foot of the altar of Baal, too tired to even whisper to their god.
Narrator 1:	Then Elijah called to the people of Israel.
Elijah:	Come here to me.
Narrator 4:	The people came to stand by Elijah. He began to repair the altar of the Lord, which had been destroyed.
Narrator 1:	Elijah took 12 stones, one for each tribe of Israel.
Narrator 2:	He rebuilt the altar of the Lord, and he dug a trench around the altar.
Narrator 3:	Elijah carefully arranged the wood, cut the bull into pieces, and laid it on the altar.
Elijah:	Please bring me four large jars of water.
Narrator 1:	The water was brought to him.
Narrator 2:	Elijah took the jars and poured the water over the offering, wood, and altar.
Narrator 3:	Elijah did this three times, until the water filled the trench around the altar.
Narrator 5:	It was now Elijah's turn to call on the God he served.

Elijah:	God of Abraham, Isaac, and Israel, let it be known that you are God in Israel and that I am your servant. Answer me, O Lord, so that these people will know that you alone are Lord. Turn their hearts back again to you, O God.
Narrator 4:	The fire of the Lord fell and burned up the sacrifice, the wood, the stones, the soil, and even the water in the trench.
Narrator 1:	The people were amazed by what they saw and fell on the ground in fear.
People of Israel:	The Lord—he is God! The Lord—he is God!
Elijah:	Seize the prophets of Baal. Don't let anyone get away!
Narrator 5:	The prophets of Baal were seized, and Elijah killed them in the Kishon Valley.
Narrator 2:	Elijah then turned to Ahab.
Elijah:	Go, eat and drink, for there is the sound of a heavy rain.
Narrator 3:	Ahab went to eat and drink. Elijah climbed to the top of Mount Carmel, bent down to the ground, and prayed for God to lift the curse of the famine.
Narrator 2:	Elijah told his servant to go and look to the sea.
Elijah's servant:	Nothing is happening.
Narrator 1:	Seven times Elijah sent his servant to look toward the sea.
Narrator 2:	The seventh time the servant returned with news.
Elijah's servant:	A cloud the size of a man's hand is rising from the sea.
Elijah:	Go. Tell Ahab to hitch up his chariot and return to Jezreel before the rains stop him.
Narrator 3:	The sky became black and heavy with clouds.
Narrator 4:	The wind rose, and a heavy rain began to fall as Ahab rode off.
Narrator 5:	The power of the Lord came upon Elijah, and he ran ahead of Ahab's chariot 12 miles to Jezreel.

Elijah

Name _____

Find the answers for this crossword puzzle in 1 Kings 17–19.

Across

3. The widow lived here.
5. He ran ahead of Ahab all the way to Jezreel.
8. She was Ahab's wife.
10. Elijah hid in this ravine.
11. God sent fire down to burn up Elijah's _____.
13. This was Elijah's job.
16. The widow had only a handful of this left.
17. Elijah did this to the prophets of Baal.
19. The prophets of Baal cut themselves with swords and spears. Another word for sharp weapons like these is _____.
20. God showed his power to Israel on this mountain.

Down

1. Elijah left his servant here.
2. Obadiah hid 100 prophets in these.
4. He appeared to Elijah in the desert near Horeb.
6. Elijah fled to this mountain.
7. He was the king of Israel.
9. God sent this after the wind and before the fire.
12. He was in charge of Ahab's palace.
14. The famine was severe here.
15. God showed this on Mount Carmel.
16. This was a result of no rain.
18. Elijah asked this woman for bread.

Called by God Report

God has chosen many people to perform a special task or life work. This is seen in the lives of many biblical characters. He continues to call and use people today.

Choose a modern Christian in full-time Christian ministry. Conduct an interview to discover what his or her ministry entails and how this individual knew God's will for him or her. This could be a missionary with whom you could correspond by e-mail. You could also interview someone from your church or family. Perhaps you can discover how diligence, love, obedience, and commitment have played a role in their ministry.

Prepare a list of questions here and on the back of this page to prepare for your interview. Leave room below each question to write in the answers.

_____

_____

_____

_____

_____

_____

_____

_____

_____

_____

_____

_____

_____

_____

_____

Ahab and Ben-Hadad

Name _____

Read 1 Kings 20, and answer the following questions.

1. Why did King Ahab give in to Ben-Hadad's demands? _____
   _____

2. What demand of Ben-Hadad did King Ahab refuse? _____
   _____
   _____

3. Who told King Ahab that he would defeat the Arameans? _____
   _____
   _____

4. Why did Ben-Hadad attack the Israelites again? _____
   _____
   _____
   _____

5. Why did Ben-Hadad's officials wear sackcloth? _____
   _____
   _____

6. Why did God protect the Israelites from the Arameans even though Ahab was an evil king?
   _____
   _____

7. What did Ahab do that made God angry? _____
   _____
   _____

8. What was Ahab's punishment for his sin? _____
   _____

9. What was Israel's punishment for this sin? _____
   _____

Ahab and Naboth's Vineyard

Name _____

Narrator: Ahab, the king of Israel, was sitting on his roof one evening. He noticed a beautiful vineyard nearby. He decided that he wanted it.

Ahab: Gehar!

Gehar: Yes, your majesty.

Ahab: Find out who that vineyard belongs to, and bring the owner to me.

Gehar: Yes, your majesty. *(He hurries off and returns a while later with Naboth.)* Here is Naboth, the owner of the vineyard.

Ahab: Naboth, your vineyard is close to my garden. Let me have it for a vegetable garden. I'll give you a better vineyard, or, if you like, I'll pay you for it.

Naboth: Your majesty, the Lord forbid that I should sell you my vineyard.

Ahab: What do you mean you won't sell it to me? I want it! I said I'll get you another vineyard.

Naboth: My father left this vineyard to me, and his father left it to him. It's our family inheritance in the Promised Land. According to the laws of our land, I have to keep it as an inheritance for my children.

Ahab: Go away! I don't want to talk to you anymore. You're too stubborn.

Narrator: Ahab went to his room and sulked. Later Jezebel went to him.

Jezebel: What's the matter with you? Why aren't you eating?

Ahab: I'm angry. I want Naboth's vineyard. I asked him to sell it to me or to let me give him another vineyard for it, but he refused. He says that it's his inheritance and that he must give it to his children.

Jezebel: You're the king, aren't you? You sure aren't acting like it. Leave everything to me. Get up and eat! I'll get you Naboth's vineyard.

Narrator: Jezebel wrote letters to the elders and nobles of the city. She wrote:

Jezebel:	Proclaim a day of fasting, and set Naboth in a high place among the people. But set two scoundrels across from him, and have them testify that he has cursed God and the king. Then take him out and stone him to death.
Narrator:	She sealed the letters with Ahab's seal and sent them out. The elders did as she had ordered. Later they sent a messenger to Jezebel.
Messenger:	Your majesty, Naboth has been stoned. He is dead.
Narrator:	When Ahab heard the news, he stopped sulking and got up.
Ahab:	Jezebel, how did you work that out? I'm going to go check out my new vineyard right now!
Narrator:	But things were not settled yet. God had seen what Ahab and Jezebel had done. He sent the prophet Elijah to Naboth's vineyard to meet Ahab.
Ahab:	So you have found me, my enemy!
Elijah:	I have found you because you are so wicked. You have murdered a man and taken his property. Because of this and all the other evil you have done, your whole family will die. In the place where dogs licked up Naboth's blood, dogs will lick up your blood. And dogs will eat Jezebel by the wall of Jezreel. Your family members who die in the city will be eaten by the dogs. The birds of the air will feed on those who die in the country.
Narrator:	Ahab felt sorry for what he had done, and he fasted and wore sackcloth. God decided to postpone the punishment. God told Elijah, "I will not bring this disaster in his day, but I will bring it on his house in the days of his son."

Ahab and Naboth's Vineyard

Name

1 Kings 21 Write out the applicable part of the verse and tell how it relates to this story.

1.	Ahab wanted Naboth's vineyard and was miserable without it.	**Exodus 20:17**
2.	Ahab sulked and refused to eat.	**Hebrews 13:5**
3.	Jezebel schemed to slander Naboth.	**Titus 3:1–2**
4.	Two scoundrels brought false charges against Naboth.	**Exodus 20:16**
5.	Naboth was stoned to death.	**Exodus 20:13**
6.	Ahab got up and went down to take possession of the vineyard.	**Exodus 20:15**
7.	Elijah confronted Ahab with his sin.	**Luke 17:3**

Ahab's Defeat

Name _____

Answer the following questions from 1 Kings 22, in the second column, and apply what you learn to your own life. (The first one is done for you.)

1. Before Jehoshaphat, king of Judah, agreed to go to war with King Ahab, what did he wisely seek?	He wanted the counsel of the Lord. I need to seek the counsel of the Lord.
2. After receiving the counsel of Ahab's 400 prophets, what did Jehoshaphat still ask?	
3. After Micaiah sarcastically told King Ahab what he wanted to hear, what was his true message?	
4. How did Ahab respond to God's word?	

5. How was God merciful to

   Jehoshaphat?

6. How were the prophecies of both

   Elijah and Micaiah fulfilled?

Elijah to Elisha

In each cloud write a way that God showed his power in 2 Kings 2.

Name

Who Said?

Write down the name of the person or people who made each of these statements.
Use your Bible if you need help.

1. "There will be neither dew nor rain" (I Kings 17:1).

_____

2. "I have ordered the ravens to feed you" (1 Kings 17:4).

_____

3. "I don't have any bread" (1 Kings 17:12).

_____

4. "Give me your son" (1 Kings 17:19).

_____

5. "I hid a hundred of the LORD's prophets" (1 Kings 18:13).

_____

6. "Is that you, you troubler of Israel?" (1 Kings 18:17).

_____

7. "O Baal, answer us!" (1 Kings 18:26).

_____

8. "The LORD—he is God!" (1 Kings 18:39).

_____

9. "A cloud as small as a man's hand is rising from the sea" (1 Kings 18:44).

_____

10. "May the gods deal with me, be it ever so severely, if by this time tomorrow I do not make your life like that of one of them" (1 Kings 19:2).

_____

11. "I have had enough, LORD" (1 Kings 19:4).

_____

12. "Let me kiss my father and mother good-by" (1 Kings 19:20).

_____

13. "Your silver and gold are mine, and the best of your wives and children are mine" (1 Kings 20:2–3).

_____

14. "Do you see this vast army? I will give it into your hand today" (1 Kings 20:13).

15. "Their gods are gods of the hills" (1 Kings 20:23).

16. "Is he still alive? He is my brother" (1 Kings 20:32).

17. "The LORD forbid that I should give you the inheritance of my fathers" (1 Kings 21:3).

18. "Is this how you act as king over Israel? . . . I'll get you the vineyard . . ." (1 Kings 21:7).

19. "In the place where dogs licked up Naboth's blood, dogs will lick up your blood—yes, yours!" (1 Kings 21:19).

20. "Is there not a prophet of the LORD here whom we can inquire of?" (1 Kings 22:7).

21. "As surely as the LORD lives, I can tell him only what the LORD tells me" (1 Kings 22:14).

22. "Didn't I tell you that he never prophesies anything good about me, but only bad?" (1 Kings 22:18).

23. "I will enter the battle in disguise, but you wear your royal robes" (1 Kings 22:30).

24. "Do you know that the LORD is going to take your master from you today?" (2 Kings 2:5).

25. "Let me inherit a double portion of your spirit" (2 Kings 2:9).

26. "The spirit of Elijah is resting on Elisha" (2 Kings 2:15).

Ahab the Awful

Name _____

Fill in the blanks with the correct words.

1 Kings 20

Ahab was king over __ __ __ __ __ __. The city of

__ __ __ __ __ __ __ was attacked by Ben-Hadad, king of

__ __ __ __. He demanded all of the silver and gold and the best

of the wives and children, and King Ahab gave in to him. Then

__ __ __ – __ __ __ __ __ demanded to search Ahab's

__ __ __ __ __ __ so that he could seize anything he wanted.

Ahab would not let him, so Ben-Hadad prepared to attack Samaria.

Then a prophet of the __ __ __ __ came to Ahab and told him,

"The Lord will help you win the battle." So Ahab fought the Arameans,

and the Lord gave him a great victory. The Arameans believed that Israel's God was god only

of the __ __ __ __ __, so they attacked the Israelites the next __ __ __ __ __ __ on the

plains. God wanted the Arameans to know that he was Lord of all, so he again gave the victory

to the Israelites. Ben-Hadad ran away and __ __ __. His officials said, "We heard that Israel's

king is __ __ __ __ __ __ __ __. Perhaps he will spare your __ __ __ __." They went to

Ahab and asked him to spare Ben-Hadad. Ahab said, "Is he still alive? He is my

__ __ __ __ __ __ __." Ben-Hadad and Ahab made a __ __ __ __ __ __, and Ahab set

Ben-Hadad free. God was angry with Ahab. God had helped Israel defeat the Arameans, but

Ahab had let Ben-Hadad go free. Ahab would die because of this disobedience.

1 Kings 21

__ __ __ __ __ __ had a __ __ __ __ __ __ __ __ that Ahab wanted. When Naboth

refused to sell it to him, Ahab became __ __ __ __ __. His wife Jezebel __ __ __ __ letters

to the __ __ __ __ __ __ and nobles in Naboth's city, arranging to have Naboth stoned for

__ __ __ __ __ __ __ God and the king. Ahab then took the vineyard. __ __ __ __ __ __

told Ahab that God would punish him for murdering Naboth.

1 Kings 22:1–28

Ahab asked ___ __ __ __ __ __ __ __ __ __ __, king of Judah, to help him fight
                                        23

against ___ __ __ __ __ __   __ __ __ __ __. When they called in the
                 24   25

___ __ __ __ __ __ __ Micaiah to ask him about it, he told them that Ahab would
   26   27

be killed in the battle. Ahab said, "Take Micaiah and put him in prison, and give him

nothing but bread and water until I return safely from battle." But King Ahab was wounded

during the battle and ___ __ __ ___. Later the dogs licked up his blood, just as the
                        28

Lord had declared.

Now fill in the spaces with the correct letters from the words above.
Use the letters that correspond with the numbers.

___ ___ ___ ___ ___ ___   ___ ___   ___ ___ ___ ___ ___ ___ ___ ___
 1   2   3   4   5   6   7   8   9 10 11 12 13 14 15 16

___ ___ ___   ___ ___ ___ ___ ___ ___ ___ ___ ___ .
17 18 19   20 21 22 23 24 25 26 27 28

God Shows His Care and Power

Choose one of the miracles recorded in 2 Kings 4:38—44. Fill in the sections of the comic strip below with pictures and dialogue. Use the first box for the title of your comic strip and your name. Add dialogue balloons where you need them in the rest of the boxes.

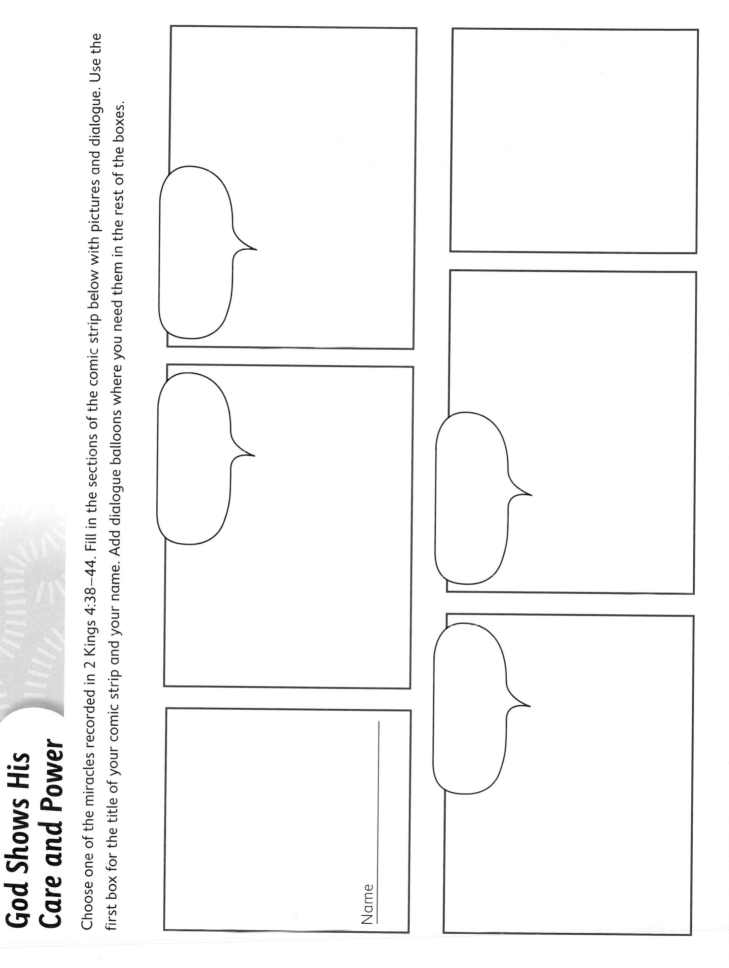

Name _____

The Servant Girl and Naaman

Use the clues on the following page, along with 2 Kings 5, to fill in the answers to the puzzle. The box will give you the theme of this lesson.

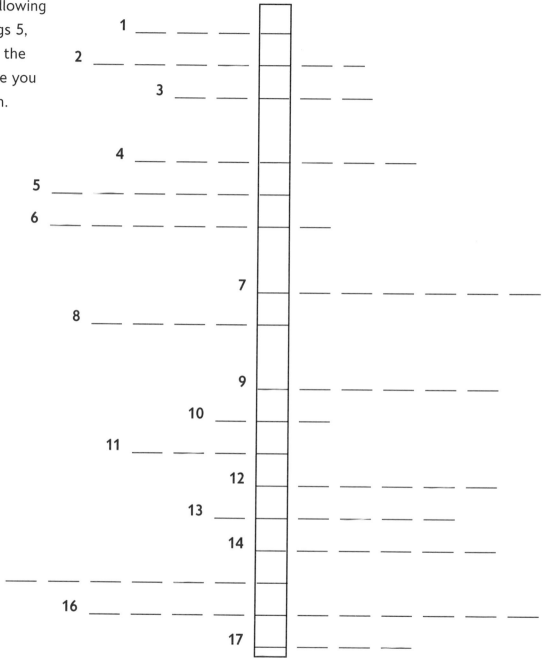

1 ___ ___ ___

2 ___ ___ ___ ___   ___ ___

3 ___ ___   ___ ___

4 ___ ___ ___   ___ ___

5 ___ ___ ___ ___

6 ___ ___ ___ ___

7 ___ ___ ___ ___ ___

8 ___ ___ ___ ___

9 ___ ___ ___ ___

10 ___   ___

11 ___ ___ ___

12 ___ ___ ___

13 ___   ___

14 ___ ___ ___

15 ___ ___ ___ ___ ___   ___

16 ___ ___ ___   ___

17 ___ ___ ___

1. Naaman was the commander of the _____ of Aram.

2. He suffered from the disease of _____.

3. Bands from Aram had taken a _____ girl, and she served Naaman's wife.

4. The girl told Naaman's wife that Naaman should go see the prophet in _____.

5. The king of Aram sent a _____ to the king of Israel.

6. The king of Israel thought he was trying to pick a _____ with him.

7. Elisha sent the _____ to have Naaman come to him.

8. Naaman went away _____ when he was given the message to go wash in the Jordan River seven times.

9. Naaman thought his own rivers were better than the _____ of Israel.

10. Naaman's servants persuaded him to _____ in the water seven times, as Elisha had said.

11. Naman's flesh was restored, and he returned to Elisha and offered him a _____.

12. Even though _____ urged him, he refused.

13. _____ thought Elisha was too easy on Naaman.

14. Gehazi followed Naaman, caught up with him, and asked for _____ and clothing.

15. Naaman gladly gave him two _____ of silver and two sets of clothing.

16. As a punishment, Naaman's leprosy would cling to Gehazi and to his _____ forever.

17. Gehazi left Elisha and was leprous, as white as _____.

The Floating Axhead

Name _____

Draw the picture or fill in the explanation from the story in 2 Kings 6:1–6.

_____

_____

As one of them was cutting down a tree by the Jordan River, the axhead fell into the water.

_____

_____

Elisha cut a stick and threw it into the water where the axhead had dropped.

_____

Elisha Traps Blinded Arameans

Narrator:	The king of Aram was at war with Israel and was not happy!
King of Aram:	Soldiers, what is happening? We've set up so many ambushes, but those Israelites are expecting us every time. We must have a traitor among us! Which one of you is telling them our plans?
Officer:	My lord, it's not anyone here. It's that prophet Elisha. You whisper something in your bedroom, and somehow he knows about it! He is the one who keeps telling the king of Israel our plans.
King of Aram:	Where is this Elisha?
Soldier 1:	He's in Dothan, sir.
King of Aram:	Gather your troops. Get the horses and chariots. Go tonight and capture this troublemaker!
Narrator:	The next morning Elisha's servant got up and went outside. The sight terrified him—the city was surrounded by an army with horses and chariots.
Servant:	Oh, my lord, what are we going to do? We're all going to die!
Elisha:	Don't be afraid. We've got them outnumbered.
Servant:	Outnumbered? Just look at them all!
Elisha (in prayer):	Lord, open his eyes.
Servant (in awe):	I can't believe it! The hills are full of horses and chariots of fire. We really do outnumber them!
Narrator:	The enemy, the Arameans, began to advance toward Elisha.
Elisha:	Lord, strike these people with blindness.
Soldier 2:	What happened? I've got something in my eye!
Soldier 3:	It's dark! I can't see either. Hey, can anybody see?
Soldier 1:	No, it must be some magical spell. It's pitch dark.
Soldier 2:	Should we turn back? What are we going to do?
Narrator:	Just then, Elisha approached them.
Elisha:	Men, this way! You're on the wrong road. I'll lead you to that man you're looking for.
Officer:	Let's go, men. We have no other choice. Maybe there will be light there.

Narrator:	The Arameans followed Elisha to the city of Samaria, where they were surrounded by Israelite soldiers.
Elisha:	Lord, open the eyes of these men.
Narrator:	Suddenly the men could see and were terrified.
Soldier 3:	What's this? This isn't Dothan! We've been tricked!
Soldiers 1–3:	We're dead! We're all dead!
King of Israel:	Elisha, this is amazing! You've brought our enemy right to us! Shall we kill them?
Elisha:	Kill our guests? No! Bring them a meal. They must be hungry after the day they've had.
King of Israel:	Servants, prepare a feast for our guests.
Narrator:	After the Arameans had finished eating and drinking, they were sent home. From then on, the bands from Aram stopped raiding Israel's territory.

The Rest of the Story

Name _____

Imagine that you are a soldier returning to Aram. You still can't believe what has just happened. Fill in the sections of the comic strip below with pictures and dialogue of what may have been the rest of the story as you returned to your home. Use the first box for the title of your comic strip and your name. Add dialogue balloons where you need them in the rest of the boxes.

Name _____

Famine in Besieged Samaria

Name _____

Indicate whether the following statements are true or false. Explain why the false statements are false. You may use 2 Kings 6:24—7:20 to help you.

1. Ben-Hadad and his entire army laid siege to Samaria. _____
   _____

2. Food continued to be plentiful in the city. _____
   _____

3. The king of Israel confessed his sin and took responsibility for what was happening. _____
   _____

4. Elisha predicted that within 24 hours, food would again be plentiful. _____
   _____

5. The king of Israel doubted Elisha's words. _____
   _____

6. Six lepers decided to go to the Aramean camp to beg for mercy. _____
   _____

7. They found the camp deserted, with food and belongings left behind. _____
   _____

8. The lepers immediately told the good news to the people of Samaria. _____
   _____

9. The king thanked God for saving them. _____
   _____

10. The officer who had doubted Elisha's words was trampled to death. _____
    _____

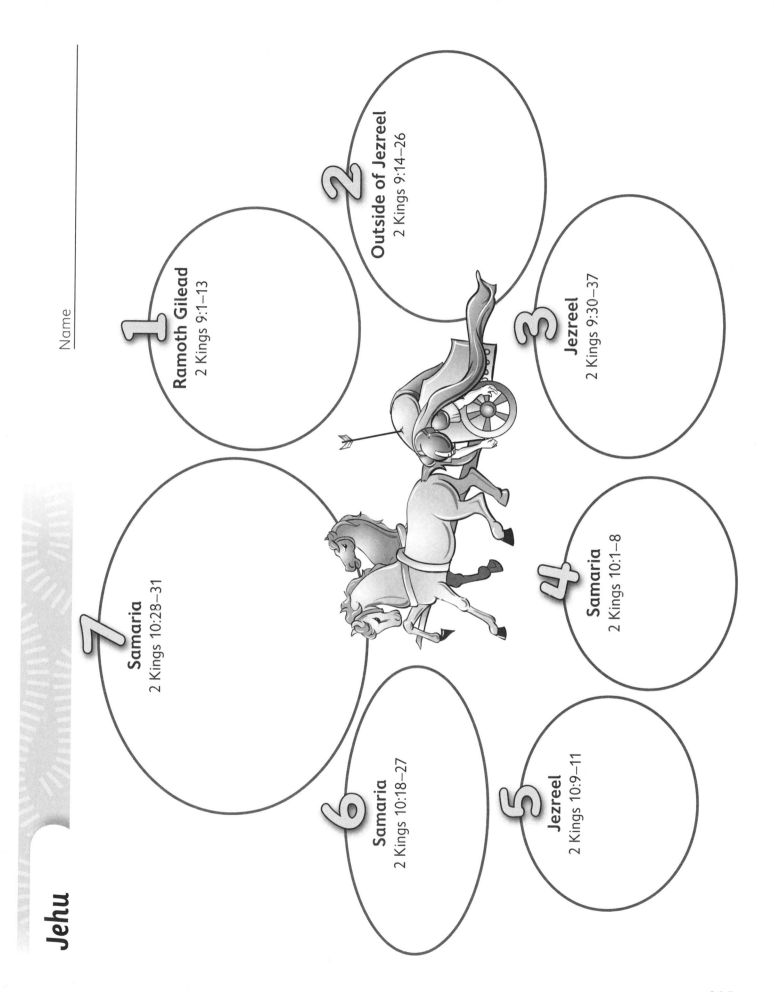

Name _____

Jehu

1 **Ramoth Gilead**
2 Kings 9:1–13

2 **Outside of Jezreel**
2 Kings 9:14–26

3 **Jezreel**
2 Kings 9:30–37

4 **Samaria**
2 Kings 10:1–8

5 **Jezreel**
2 Kings 10:9–11

6 **Samaria**
2 Kings 10:18–27

7 **Samaria**
2 Kings 10:28–31

Jehoshaphat Obeyed God

Name _____

God's Commands	Jehoshaphat's Obedience
1. Have no other gods before me.	2 Chronicles 17:6
2. Write the commandments upon your hearts.	2 Chronicles 17:9
3. Inquire of the Lord what his will is.	2 Chronicles 18:6
4. Deal justly with others.	2 Chronicles 19:4–7
5. Trust in the Lord.	2 Chronicles 20:3–12
6. Worship the Lord.	2 Chronicles 20:18–19
7. Praise the Lord.	2 Chronicles 20:21, 27–28

1. What were two of Jehoshaphat's mistakes?

   a. 2 Chronicles 18:1—19:3 _____

   b. 2 Chronicles 20:35–37 _____

2. How did Jehoshaphat provide a good example for us to follow? _____

   _____

   _____

   _____

3. Write out the last sentence of 2 Chronicles 20:12 _____

   _____

   How could this verse apply to your life? _____

   _____

King Jehoram

Think back to the way that Judah was blessed when the kings served God. Draw a picture of what a family, town, or farm in Judah may have looked like when a king who served God was reigning.

Think about what life was like under the reign of King Jehoram. Draw a picture of that same family, town, or farm under Jehoram's rule.

Ahaziah, Athaliah, and Joash

Name _____

Becoming King—2 Chronicles 22:10—24:1

1. Why didn't Athaliah kill Joash? _____

   _____

2. Describe the scene when Joash was crowned. _____

   _____

   _____

3. What happened when Athaliah heard the news? _____

   _____

   _____

4. How old was Joash when he became king? _____

Serving God—2 Chronicles 24:2–14

5. Who guided young king Joash? _____

   _____

6. What did Joash do with the foreign gods in Judah? _____

   _____

   _____

7. How did Joash go about restoring the temple? _____

   _____

   _____

8. How did God bless the people during this time? _____

   _____

   _____

Rejecting God—2 Chronicles 24:15–24

9. How old was Jehoiada when he died? _____

_____

10. Why do you think God allowed him to live so long? _____

_____

_____

11. What did Joash do when he followed his friends' bad advice? _____

_____

_____

12. Who was Zechariah, and why was he killed? _____

_____

_____

13. What happened to the people of Judah when they abandoned God? _____

_____

_____

Your teacher will assign you one of the following Bible references. Read the passage, illustrate it on another sheet of paper, and write a short summary of it at the bottom of your picture.

	2 Chronicles 23:9–10	2 Chronicles 24:9–10
	2 Chronicles 23:11	2 Chronicles 24:11
	2 Chronicles 23:12–13	2 Chronicles 24:12–13
	2 Chronicles 23:14–15	2 Chronicles 24:14
2 Kings 8:25–29	2 Chronicles 23:16–17	2 Chronicles 24:15–16
2 Chronicles 22:7–9	2 Chronicles 23:18–19	2 Chronicles 24:17–18
2 Chronicles 22:10	2 Chronicles 23:20–21	2 Chronicles 24:19
2 Chronicles 22:11–12	2 Chronicles 24:1–5	2 Chronicles 24:20–22
2 Chronicles 23:1–3	2 Chronicles 24:6–7	2 Chronicles 24:23–24
2 Chronicles 23:4–8	2 Chronicles 24:8	2 Chronicles 24:25–27

Kings of Israel

Unscramble the names of the kings of Israel described in 2 Kings 13–15.
Then fill in the blanks using the names.
Remember to capitalize the first
letter of each name.

shaoejh

khaep

mallshu   bmejaoro II   nhmemea

harziecha   pheahiak   eajhzaoh

1. _____ was king when Hazael and Ben-Hadad oppressed Israel. He sought God's favor, and God delivered Israel from Aram, but the Israelites still worshiped the golden calves (13:1–6).

2. _____ defeated Ben-Hadad three times and retook several Israelite towns (13:25).

3. _____ was allowed by God to defeat Israel's enemies because Israel was suffering greatly (14:26–27).

4. _____ reigned for only six months and then was assassinated (15:8–10).

5. _____ was king for only one month and then was assassinated (15:13–14).

6. _____ taxed the rich men 50 shekels of silver to give to the king of Assyria (15:19–20).

7. _____ was assassinated by his own army officers (15:23–25).

8. _____ reigned for 20 years and was then assassinated (15:27–30).

Plagues and Promises

An invasion of locusts brought destruction to the people of Judah. Joel 1 describes the damage the locusts created. In each locust write one example of what was destroyed.

Joel promised that if the people returned to God, their lives would change. Joel 2:12–32 promises that God would bless the people if they turned their hearts to him. In each heart write an example of God's blessings.

Four More Kings

King Amaziah—2 Kings 14:1–22

King Amaziah reigned for _____ years. He did what was _____ in God's eyes, but not as David had done. He did not remove the _____ _____, and people continued to offer _____ there. Amaziah defeated the _____. After this, he challenged Jehoash, king of _____, to fight him. Jehoash told him, "You are _____. Why ask for trouble?" Israel attacked Judah, and Judah was defeated. Jehoash captured _____. He broke down the wall of _____, and he took all the gold, silver, and other articles found in the Lord's _____. Amaziah turned away from the Lord. He was _____ by his enemies at Lachish.

King Uzziah—2 Chronicles 26

Uzziah was _____ years old when he became king. He reigned for _____ years. He did what was _____ in the eyes of the Lord. Uzziah had a large and well-trained _____. He became a very _____ king. Uzziah became proud and _____ to God. He entered the temple of the Lord to burn _____ on the altar. The priests told him, "It is not for you to burn incense to the Lord. That is for the _____ to do. Leave the temple." Uzziah became _____, but while he was yelling at the priests in the temple, _____ broke out on his forehead. King Uzziah had leprosy until the day he _____.

King Jotham—2 Chronicles 27

King Jotham reigned _____ years. He did what was _____ in the eyes of the Lord. But the people of Judah were _____. Jotham conquered the _____ in war. He brought much prosperity and wealth to the people of Judah. He became _____ because he walked in the ways of the Lord.

King Ahaz—2 Chronicles 28

Ahaz was the worst of all of the kings of Judah. He reigned for _____

years and did _____ do what was _____ in the Lord's eyes. Ahaz

made _____ for worshiping Baal, burned sacrifices to Baal, and even

sacrificed his own children. The Arameans and the _____ both defeated Ahaz in war, and

took some people of Judah as captives. The prophet _____ warned the Israelites that God

was angry with them for taking the captives, and Israel let them go.

Ahaz had more problems. Judah was attacked by the _____ and the _____.

The Lord humbled Judah because Ahaz had brought _____ to the land. In all this trouble

Ahaz did not turn to God but became more _____. He sacrificed to false gods, but they

did not _____ him. Ahaz closed the temple, set up altars at every street corner in

Jerusalem, and built high places in every town to sacrifice to other gods. This caused the Lord

to become _____.

Amaziah, Uzziah, Jotham, Ahaz

Name _____

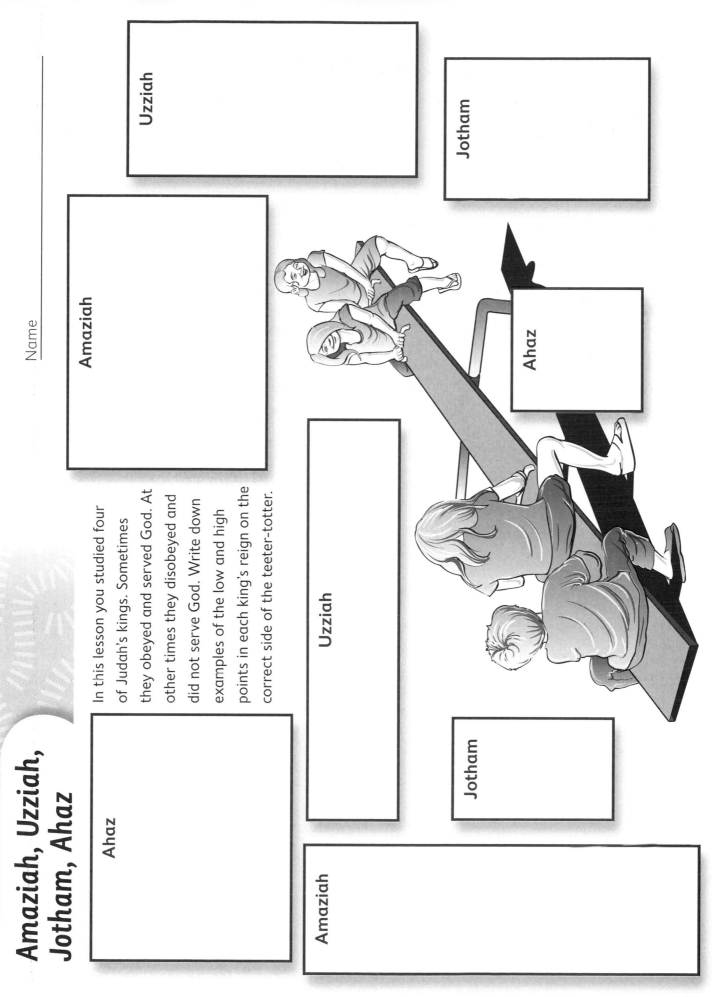

Uzziah

Jotham

Amaziah

Ahaz

In this lesson you studied four of Judah's kings. Sometimes they obeyed and served God. At other times they disobeyed and did not serve God. Write down examples of the low and high points in each king's reign on the correct side of the teeter-totter.

Uzziah

Ahaz

Jotham

Amaziah

Amos

Amos was a shepherd chosen to give a message from God. Like many prophets, his message included these three topics: sin, judgment, and mercy. Read the following Scripture passages from the Book of Amos and answer the questions.

Sin

1. Who would God's judgment come upon in chapter 1 and in the first part of chapter 2?

   (Use the chapter titles for help.) _____

2. God would also judge Israel. Name some the sins of which Israel was guilty.

   a. Amos 4:4 _____

   b. Amos 5:11 _____

   c. Amos 5:12 _____

   d. Amos 6:4–6 _____

   e. Amos 6:8, 13 _____

Judgment

3. Because of Israel's sin, God would bring punishment. Tell what would happen.

   a. Amos 3:11 _____

   b. Amos 4:6 _____

   c. Amos 4:7 _____

   d. Amos 4:9 _____

   e. Amos 4:10 _____

   f. Amos 8:11 _____

4. Along with his warnings, God offered mercy. Write down what the following verses say would happen if the people repented.

   a. Amos 5:4, 6, 14 _____

   b. Amos 9:8 _____

   c. Amos 9:13 _____

   d. Amos 9:14 _____

5. Amos spoke of hope for the world through the house of Jacob. How did this hope become a reality? _____

Amos's Visions

God showed Amos five visions that told of his coming judgment on Israel. Choose one of the visions below to explain and illustrate.

1. Locusts (Amos 7:1–3)

2. Fire (Amos 7:4–6)

3. Plumb line (Amos 7:7–9)

4. Basket of ripe fruit (Amos 8:1–3)

5. The Lord standing at the altar (Amos 9:1–10)

Vision: _____

Explanation: _____

_____

_____

_____

_____

_____

_____

Hosea Tells of God's Love

The theme of the Book of Hosea involves God's tremendous love for his people despite all their sin. Hosea's relationship with his wife is the chief example of this teaching. Scripture is full of references to God's love for us.

1. Look up the following verses and write what you learn from them about God's love. Use personal pronouns to make your writing personal.

Romans 8:35–39

Jeremiah 31:3

John 3:16

Psalm 17:7–8

Zephaniah 3:17

1 John 3:1

2. Write responses to the following question in the objects below:

How can we show our love for God?

Hezekiah

Name _____

Narrator 1: Hezekiah became king over Judah when he was 25 years old. He ruled in Jerusalem for 29 years.

Narrator 2: Israel finally had a king who did what was right in the eyes of the Lord, like David had done.

Hezekiah: All of the foreign idols and high places had to be destroyed!

Narrator 3: Hezekiah trusted the Lord in all things and kept his commands.

Narrator 4: During Hezekiah's reign the Assyrians conquered the Israelites. The people of Israel were taken into captivity, and their kingdom was destroyed. This happened because the people of Israel had not obeyed God and had repeatedly violated his covenant.

Narrator 5: Sennacherib, the king of Assyria, then moved south and attacked all of the fortified cities of Judah.

Hezekiah (to Sennacherib): Let's make a deal. I'll pay you lots of money if you stop attacking us.

Narrator 1: All of the gold that covered the temple doors was given to Sennacherib as part of the tribute.

Sennacherib: That's not good enough.

Narrator 2: Sennacherib sent his field commander, along with a large army, to Jerusalem.

Narrator 3: The field commander called to the people of Jerusalem in their own language.

Assyrian field commander:	I have news for you from Sennacherib, the great king of Assyria.
Joah:	I'm guessing that this is not something we want to hear.
Assyrian field commander:	You seem to think that you'll be able to defend yourselves against the great people of Assyria and escape the disaster that met your brothers, the Israelites. You are foolish, foolish people.
Eliakim:	Joah, this is not looking good.
Assyrian field commander:	If you depend on God, you are really, really foolish. Your king destroyed the high places, so now you can worship only in one place. Why would you trust in a God who can be worshiped only in Jerusalem? Your God told me to march against this country and destroy it.
Joah:	He's lying. God would never tell him to destroy us. We're God's chosen people!
Eliakim:	Look at the people. This commander is making them upset, and they're losing hope.
Shebna:	Commander, thank you for your words of warning and concern. Please speak in Aramaic. Don't speak in Hebrew—you're scaring the people.
Joah:	Good idea, Shebna. If he speaks in Aramiac, most of the people won't understand what he's saying.
Assyrian field commander:	My master, the king of Assyria, sent me to speak to all of the people in Jerusalem. I will speak in Hebrew so that everyone will understand my words. Don't let Hezekiah deceive you by saying that the Lord will deliver you from us. Surely the Lord will deliver this city into the hands of the Assyrians. If you surrender to us now, you will avoid certain death. Don't trust in your God and in Hezekiah.
Shebna (quietly to his men):	Send word to Hezekiah of the commander's words. Tell all of the people to be quiet and not to answer the commander's taunts.
Narrator 3:	When Hezekiah heard what had happened, he tore his clothes, put on sackcloth, and went to the temple of the Lord.
Hezekiah:	God, what shall I do? Please save your people from the Assyrians.
Narrator 4:	God heard Hezekiah's pleas and sent his prophet Isaiah to speak with Hezekiah.
Isaiah:	This is what the Lord Almighty says: The king of Assyria will not enter this city or shoot an arrow here. I will defend the city and save it from its enemies.
Narrator 5:	That night the angel of the Lord killed 185,000 Assyrian soldiers.
Narrator 4:	When King Sennacherib left his tent and saw all of the dead, he broke camp and returned to Nineveh.

Hot off the Press

Name _____

Write a newspaper article about the attack of Assyria on Israel. Name your paper, write a headline for the story, and include your name as the author. Draw a picture to go along with the story, and write a caption for it.

722 B.C.   VOL. 500

Isaiah's Call and My Call

Name _____

1. Number the following 10 events describing Isaiah's call to service in Isaiah 6 according to the order in which they happened.

   _____ **a.** The Lord asked, "Whom shall I send? And who will go for us?"

   _____ **b.** The doors of the temple shook, and the temple was filled with smoke.

   _____ **c.** The land would be destroyed but a holy seed would be left.

   _____ **d.** A seraph touched Isaiah's mouth with a live coal.

   _____ **e.** Isaiah saw the Lord, high and exalted.

   _____ **f.** "For how long, O Lord?" Isaiah asked.

   _____ **g.** "Woe to me! I am ruined!" Isaiah cried.

   _____ **h.** "Here am I. Send me!" Isaiah said.

   _____ **i.** Seraphs were flying and worshiping.

   _____ **j.** The Lord said to tell the people that they would be ever hearing but never understanding.

2. What does God call you to do? Find examples in the following verses.

   (The first one is done for you.)

   a. Isaiah 43:10 ___Be his witness._____

   b. John 1:12 _____

   c. Romans 13:1 _____

   d. 2 Corinthians 9:7 _____

   e. Ephesians 6:1 _____

   f. Philippians 4:6 _____

   g. Colossians 3:23 _____

   h. 1 John 4:7 _____

3. How does God want you to respond to his call? Write out Jesus' answer in John 14:15. _____

   _____

Judah's Sin and God's Judgment

Your teacher will assign you one or more Scripture passages to look up. Write a one- or two-sentence summary of your assigned passage or passages.

Sin

1. Isaiah 1:2–4 _____

    _____

2. Isaiah 1:13 _____

    _____

3. Isaiah 1:23 _____

    _____

4. Isaiah 2:6–8 _____

    _____

5. Isaiah 2:22 _____

6. Isaiah 3:16–24 _____

    _____

Judgment

7. Isaiah 1:7 _____

    _____

8. Isaiah 1:15–16 _____

    _____

9. Isaiah 1:28 _____

    _____

10. Isaiah 2:17 _____

    _____

God's Mercy

11. Micah 2:12 _____

_____

12. Micah 5:6 _____

_____

13. Micah 7:18–20 _____

_____

14. Isaiah 1:18–19 _____

_____

15. Isaiah 4:2–6 _____

_____

_____

16. Isaiah 14:25 _____

_____

17. Isaiah 58:9–11 _____

_____

_____

18. Isaiah 61:11 _____

_____

_____

God's Mercy

Name _____

Write a short summary of these passages from the Book of Isaiah. Some are done for you.

1. **1:18** _God offers forgiveness._

2. **2:4** _There will be peace._

3. **9:6** _The Messiah will come._

4. **13–23** _____

5. **32:1** _A king will reign in righteousness._

6. **35:10** _The ransomed of the Lord will return to Zion._

7. **40:11** _God will be like a gentle shepherd._

8. **40:31** _God will renew their strength._

9. **41:13–20** _____

10. **43:2** _God will be with them in trouble._

11. **45:13** _Jerusalem will be rebuilt and exiles freed._

12. **51:3** _____

13. **51:11** _Gladness and joy will replace sorrow._

14. **54:1–8** _____

15. **54:9–17** _____

16. **55:7** _God will pardon those who repent._

17. **56:3** _Foreigners will be included in God's salvation._

18. **58:9–11** _____

19. **61:9** _____

20. **61:11** _____

21. **62:12** _____

22. **65:17** _God will create new heavens and a new earth._

Choose one passage from the list to illustrate on a larger sheet of paper as a poster. After reading the passage carefully, choose a key image or phrase. Include the verse somewhere on your picture.

Prophecies of Christ in Isaiah

Find the answers for this crossword puzzle in the Book of Isaiah. The chapter and verse are at the end of each clue.

Across

4. The Redeemer will come to Zion, to those in Jacob who _____ of their sins (59:20).
5. As a _____ before her shearers is silent, so he did not open his mouth (53:7).
7. I did not hide my face from _____ and spitting (50:6).
9. Surely he took up our infirmities and carried our _____ (53:4).
10. A voice of one calling: In the desert _____ the way for the Lord (40:3).
11. Then will the lame leap like a deer, and the mute _____ shout for joy (35:6).
12. He tends his flock like a _____: He gathers the lambs in his arms (40:11).
15. Then will the eyes of the blind be _____ and the ears of the deaf unstopped (35:5).
16. I will put my Spirit on him and he will bring _____ to the nations (42:1).
17. For to us a _____ is born (9:6).
18. He will swallow up _____ forever (25:8).

Down

1. And he will be called Wonderful Counselor, Mighty God, Everlasting Father, _____ of Peace (9:6).
2. I offered my back to those who beat me, my _____ to those who pulled out my beard (50:6).
3. A shoot will come up from the _____ of Jesse (11:1).
6. The Lord has _____ me to preach good news to the poor (61:1).
8. The virgin will be with child and will give birth to a son, and will call him _____ (7:14).
10. See, I have engraved you on the _____ of my hands (49:16).
12. See, my _____ will act wisely; he will be raised and lifted up and highly exalted (52:13).
13. He was despised and _____ by men, a man of sorrows, and familiar with suffering (53:3).
14. But he was _____ for our transgressions, he was crushed for our iniquities (53:5).

Lesson Highlights to Remember

Name

1. One-sentence summary of the Book of 2 Samuel:

    _____

    _____

    _____

2. Examples of David's obedience and faithfulness to God:

    _____

    _____

    _____

    _____

    _____

    _____

    _____

    _____

    _____

3. Examples of David's disobedience to God:

    _____

    _____

    _____

    _____

    _____

    _____

    _____

    _____

4. A summary of 1 Kings:

_____

_____

_____

_____

_____

_____

_____

_____

_____

_____

_____

_____

_____

_____

_____

5. Examples of Solomon following and disobeying God:

_____

_____

_____

_____

_____

_____

_____

_____

_____

6. Highlights and summaries of kings:

_____

_____

_____

_____

_____

_____

_____

_____

_____

_____

_____

_____

_____

_____

_____

_____

_____

_____

_____

_____

_____

_____

_____

_____

_____

Bible Dictionary

ALTARS

Sacrifices were offered to God on altars. Abraham, Isaac, and Jacob used piles of stones for their altars. Metal altars were used in the tabernacle and temple. The Israelites burned their sacrifices of grain and animals on the bronze altar of burnt offering located in the courtyard of the tabernacle and temple. Priests burned incense on the gold incense altar in the Holy Place each morning. The incense was a symbol of the people's prayers to God.

Other nations used altars to worship their idols, too. They built them on hills known as high places. Mount Carmel was a high place where God showed that he was the true God and that Baal was powerless.

Altar of Beersheva

ANOINT

Anointing with oil was very important to the Israelites. Each day they anointed themselves with olive oil to protect their skin from the hot, dry weather. This kind of anointing was similar to rubbing lotion on our skin today. The only time that oil was not rubbed on the skin was when a person was mourning.

The Israelites also used oil as perfume. They anointed themselves (dabbed their skin) with oil as a sign of gladness. The host of a banquet dabbed oil on the forehead of an honored guest.

People were anointed with oil as a sign that they had been chosen to do special work for the Lord. For example, all of Israel's kings were anointed because they were God's chosen rulers. Priests were anointed with oil before they started to work in the tabernacle or temple.

At the dedication of the tabernacle, all of the objects used for worship— altars, lampstand, table of showbread, laver, and so on—were sprinkled with holy oil before they were used.

The oil used for dedication was a special blend of pure olive oil, cinnamon, myrrh, sugar cane, and cassia tree bark. This holy oil could be made only by certain priests and could be used only for dedicating something or someone to the Lord. A person could be killed for trying to copy the recipe.

ARMOR

Soldiers in Bible times wore clothing called armor to protect themselves. Leaders wore bronze or leather helmets to protect their heads. Foot soldiers had leather breastplates to protect their chests; leaders had bronze breastplates. Soldiers carried shields for additional protection. Archers (soldiers with bows and arrows) carried small round shields, and other soldiers had large rectangular ones. Most shields were made of leather-covered wood.

The apostle Paul used the image of armor to explain how Christians are to protect themselves from the devil (Ephesians 6:13–18).

ASHTORETH

Ashtoreth was the Canaanite goddess of love and war. The Canaanites believed that no babies would be born without her consent. They also thought that plants would not produce seeds until she commanded it.

BAAL

Baal was thought to be the most powerful Canaanite god. Because bulls are so strong, the bull was a symbol for Baal. The Canaanites believed that Baal controlled the increase of crops and animals. Worship of Baal included dancing, eating, and drinking. Sometimes the priests of Baal cut themselves to try to get Baal to listen to them. When Elijah challenged the priests of Baal on Mount Carmel,

the priests became very wild because nothing happened to their altar.

BURIAL CUSTOMS

When an Israelite died, all of the family members and friends cried loudly, tore their clothes, fasted, wore sackcloth, and sat in ashes to show how sad they were. Sometimes professional mourners helped the family grieve by crying and wailing with them. The mourning usually lasted for seven days. If a king died, the mourning lasted for a month.

Because Palestine is very hot, the dead person had to be buried within 24 hours. The house in which the person had lived was considered unclean, so the family could not cook there for a period of time. Neighbors brought food, called mourning bread, and drink, called the cup of consolation.

When it was time for the burial, the body was laid on a stretcher and carried to the tomb. Family and friends

Tombs

Walking With God and His People   GRADE 4

Sarcophagus

followed, crying loudly and singing sad songs called laments. A mother might have lamented, "Alas, alas, my son!"

During Old Testament times people were not buried in coffins. If the family was poor, the body was laid in a hole or in an empty cistern and covered with rocks. Rich people were buried in a cave or tomb cut into the limestone of a hillside. Abraham bought a cave for his family to be buried in. If someone died in the desert, he or she was buried in the sand. Miriam and Aaron were buried in the sand while the Israelites were in the desert.

During New Testament times a body was wrapped in cloths, and spices were added to purify it. Some rich people were buried in coffins and placed on shelves in a family tomb or cave.

CHAMPIONS

During the time of Saul and David, it was not always the size and strength of an army that brought victory. Instead, the size of the army's champion often determined victory or defeat for the nation. Armies tried to avoid great bloodshed by sending one man from each side to fight each other. These champions, the biggest and strongest men from each side, were trained to fight one-on-one. The army of the winning champion collected slaves, possessions, and land from the army of the losing champion.

Goliath, whom David fought, was probably paid to be the champion of the Philistine army. The Philistines hoped that by sending only Goliath out to fight none of them would be killed. They paid Goliath to fight so that they wouldn't have to.

The Philistines probably thought they had a good thing going with their champion, Goliath. Since he was nine feet tall, he towered over the average men of that time, who were often only five feet two inches tall or a little taller. Think of the battle of David and Goliath as a battle between the smallest player on a soccer team and the tallest player on a basketball team. David and Goliath, however, were not playing games—they were fighting to the death.

CHARIOTS

Chariots were two-wheeled carts pulled by horses. In Bible times, chariots were an important part of warfare. Some chariots could hold three people: a warrior, a driver, and an aide or shield-bearer. The Egyptian, Canaanite, and Philistine armies had chariots. This made their armies very powerful. The Israelites did not have chariots until the time of King David.

Carving of a chariot

CLAY TABLETS

Clay was plentiful in Palestine. It was used to make pots and jars, as well as clay tablets to write on. Clean, smooth, wet clay was made into cone-shaped, drum-shaped, or flat tablets. The writing was scratched into the wet tablet, which was then baked or dried in the sun.

Clay tablets were used for writing letters, recording information, and making business contracts—much as we use paper today.

Potsherds, broken pieces of pottery, were used in the same way people today use scrap paper. Students used them to practice their writing.

COVENANT

A covenant is an agreement between two people or groups. People in Bible times took covenants very seriously. In the Old Testament there are numerous examples of God making covenants with his people. One of the most famous is God's covenant with Noah, in which God promised never again to destroy the world with a flood. God set the rainbow in the sky as a sign of this covenant.

Three types of covenants were made during Old Testament times. The first was a royal grant, a covenant made between a loyal servant and his master. The royal grant, which didn't have a set time limit, was passed down from generation to generation. The only way the servant's descendants would fail to benefit was if they left the master's service. The covenant between David and God was a royal grant.

The second type of covenant was a covenant of parity, which was made between friends or other people with similar interests. The covenant between David and Jonathan was a covenant of parity.

The third kind of covenant was a suzerain-vassal covenant, which was made between a great king and a lesser king. The great king required absolute loyalty and service from the lesser king, in exchange for protecting the lesser king and his people from enemies. The great king could force the lesser king to give him money, food, or soldiers. This covenant remained in place only as long as the two kings remained loyal to each other.

DAGON

Dagon was the Philistine god of weather and crops. After the Philistines captured Samson, they offered sacrifices to Dagon. When the Philistines captured the ark of the covenant, they placed it in Dagon's temple. The image of Dagon fell on its face before the ark twice, breaking its hands and head.

FEAST OF TABERNACLES

The Feast of Tabernacles was also called the Feast of Booths or the Feast of Ingathering. The celebration began on Tishri 15, five days after the Day of Atonement. (On the Hebrew calendar Tishri was the seventh month, roughly the same as September–October on our calendar.) During the eight-day celebration the Israelites lived in tents or booths made of branches. On the first and eighth days the Israelites ceased

Modern celebration of Feast of Tabernacles

from all normal activities and presented burnt offerings to the Lord.

The Feast of Tabernacles was a joyful time when the Israelites remembered how God had protected them during their journey through the wilderness. It was also a time to give thanks for the harvest.

GOLDEN CALVES

The Egyptians worshiped golden calves because they thought that gods in the shape of bulls or calves were powerful. When the people of Israel were waiting for Moses to return from Mount Sinai, they became discouraged. They wanted to worship a god they could see, so they asked Aaron to make a golden calf.

Later, when the kingdom was divided, King Jeroboam made golden calves for Israel to worship. The Israelites disobeyed the Lord by worshiping golden calves at Bethel and Dan. They forgot that the all-powerful God is the only true God.

GODS

The Israelites worshiped the one true God, but many of the nations around them worshiped false gods. One of the gods the Canaanites worshiped was Asherah, who was thought to be the mother of all gods. The Canaanites carved her image on poles. God commanded the Israelites to cut down all of the Asherah poles when they entered Canaan, but soon after they had settled in the land, they began to worship Asherah anyway. Many years later, Queen Jezebel encouraged the Israelites to worship Asherah, and a long time after that King Manasseh went so far as to place an Asherah pole in the temple.

Asherah statue

HIGH PLACES

A high place was an area on a roof or hilltop where an altar was made. Many people worshiped their gods in high places on roofs or hilltops, where they burned incense on an altar. They believed that the smoke from the burning incense would carry their prayers to their god.

God commanded the Israelites to destroy all of the high places in Canaan so they wouldn't be tempted to worship idols. King Jeroboam disobeyed God by placing golden calves on high places at Bethel and Dan for Israel to worship.

High place at Arad

Before the temple was built, the people worshiped the true God on a high place in Gibeon.

HOLY PLACE

The Holy Place was the largest room, located in the middle of the temple. It contained the altar of incense, 10 golden lampstands, and 12 tables with 12 loaves of bread (bread of the Presence). The 12 loaves symbolized the 12 tribes.

Each morning the priest entered the Holy Place to burn incense. Once a week priests would replace the bread with fresh bread. It was the priests' job to make sure that the lampstands were always burning.

LOCUSTS

Locusts are insects in the same family as grasshoppers, crickets, and katydids. The females lay their eggs in the sand. When the eggs hatch, the larvae eat everything in their path. Adult locusts fly in large swarms that look like dark clouds. They eat every green plant in their path. Driven by the desert winds, swarms of locusts can eat whole fields of crops. God sent swarms of locusts to Egypt as the eighth plague.

MOLECH

Molech was an Ammonite god. Once in a while the Ammonites sacrificed their children on Molech's altar. God told the Israelites never to do this, but King Ahaz sacrificed his son to Molech.

MOST HOLY PLACE

The tabernacle (and later the temple) was divided into three rooms. The room farthest away from the entrance was called the Most Holy Place (Holy of Holies). It had no windows and contained the ark of the covenant, which had two cherubim resting over the top. A priest entered the Most Holy Place only once a year, on the Day of Atonement. He offered prayers and a special sacrifice before the ark of the

Most Holy Place

covenant, asking God to forgive the sins of the people.

MUSICAL INSTRUMENTS

Orchestras in Babylon were different from today's orchestras. A flute looked more like a clarinet. Small harps called lyres were strapped across the player's shoulders. A sackbut was an instrument like a trombone. Musicians also played drums and tambourines.

Music was an important part of Israelite life. Musicians played during worship while the people sang, and they entertained during feasts or celebrations. Kings listened to music to relax. Musicians even played when an army marched into battle; the horses marched to the beat. After battle the musicians played marches or victory songs.

NAZIRITE

A Nazirite was a man or a woman who was set apart for service to God. This service to God was for a specific period of time. It could be for a short time or for a lifetime. Samson, Samuel, and John the Baptist were Nazirites all of their lives.

During their special time of service to God, Nazirites vowed (promised) not to eat or drink anything made from grapes, not to cut their hair, and not to touch anything that was dead. When the period of service was over, the Nazirite went to the priest and made certain sacrifices. Then the Nazirite shaved his or her head, because one of the sacrifices was the hair that had grown during the vow.

Samson failed to keep his vows when he touched the dead lion and when he allowed his hair to be cut.

OATHS

People throughout Old Testament times made oaths with each other, and nations made oaths with other nations. An oath was a way of guaranteeing a promise. Today we might sign a contract in the presence of others to guarantee that we will fulfill a promise. In Old Testament times God was often called upon to witness the oath, and God was asked to enforce the agreement if one of the parties involved tried to back out.

Many oaths involved not just the people who made the oath but also their descendants. Most oaths specified a punishment for breaking the oath. This punishment was also passed down to the person's children and grandchildren if the oath was not kept.

PAPYRUS

Papyrus was a writing material made from the stalk of the papyrus plant, a 12-foot plant similar to a cattail or a bulrush. A grassy, feathery flower tops each triangular stalk. Papyrus still grows along rivers and in marshy areas in Egypt.

To make papyrus writing material, the center of the stalk, called the pith, was sliced into fibers. The fibers were placed in layers to make a sheet and then soaked, hammered smooth, and dried in the sun. When the papyrus was dry, it was scraped smooth with a shell or piece of ivory. The finished papyrus sheet was creamy white.

Papyrus lasted a long time in dry places. The caves where the Dead Sea Scrolls were discovered preserved the papyrus so that it did not crumble.

Ancient people used every part of the papyrus plant. The stalks were also made into ropes, roofing material, small boats, baskets, and woven mats. The roots were used for firewood, and the flowers were made into necklaces.

Papyrus plants

PARCHMENT

Parchment is a writing material made from the skins of sheep, goats,

Parchment fragments

or calves. The skins are first soaked in lime to loosen the hair and fat, which is then scraped off. Next, the skin is stretched on a frame and thinned with knives or scrapers. Finally, the skins are rubbed with chalk or pumice to make a smooth, white writing surface. Parchment is very expensive because it takes a long time to make.

Parchment was especially popular in the ancient cities of Asia Minor. The Jews, Persians, and other ancient peoples used it for their sacred writings. Beginning about 2000 B.C., parchment replaced papyrus as the most commonly used writing material. Parchment is still used today for some important legal documents and maps.

PEN AND INK

Ancient pens were carved from dried reeds—thin, hollow grasses that grew in wet places. Some pens were shaped like brushes for writing on papyrus. Others had split, pointed ends for writing on harder parchment. A reed sharpened to a point was called a stylus.

Black ink was made by mixing carbon soot with oil or gum. Red ink for highlighting was made with red iron oxide. The mixture was dried into a cake. To write, the scribe moistened the tip of his pen with water and dipped it into the cake of ink.

Scribes made pen cases to carry their pens and ink. They carried these cases under their belts. Sometimes scribes carried a penknife for cutting papyrus and sharpening their pens.

PLUNDER

When an army attacked a city and captured it, everything in it belonged to them. The soldiers could take whatever they wanted: jewelry, other belongings, animals, and even people. The things the army took were called plunder. When Israel captured an enemy, God sometimes commanded that all of the plunder be dedicated to him. Then none of the soldiers were allowed to keep anything. David divided the plunder taken from the Philistines equally among all of the soldiers—those who had fought and those who had stayed behind.

PROPERTY

The Israelites believed that all of the world belonged to God. When the Israelites entered the Promised Land, each person or family received a portion of land, which was to belong to that family forever. The land was a symbol of God's covenant relationship with and care for his people. In hard times some people sold their land to others, knowing that they or their relatives could buy the land back when they were able.

The Israelites were to celebrate the Year of Jubilee every 50 years. At this time land was to be returned to the original owner or his descendants. God's people were always to be provided for in this way. They would never be without the ability to raise crops or to take care of their families. The Year of Jubilee also ensured that the difference between the wealthy and the poor would never became too great.

Terraces

SACKCLOTH

Sometimes a person who was sad or who knew about something bad that was going to happen to the nation wore sackcloth—a dark, coarse cloth made from goat's hair. It probably felt like a piece of burlap or a very scratchy wool sweater. The sackcloth was shaped into a garment and worn next to the skin.

Palestinian shepherds wore sackcloth because it was cheap and durable. Prophets sometimes wore sackcloth when they preached repentance.

SACRIFICE

In the Old Testament people sacrificed animals and crops to God, giving him the best of what they had. Their sacrifices were visible signs of what they felt toward God in their hearts.

One type of sacrifice was called a sin offering. For this offering an animal was brought to the altar. Before the animal was sacrificed, the person bringing the sacrifice placed his hands on the animal to show that his sins were being transferred to the animal. The priest then killed the animal and sprinkled the blood on the altar before sacrificing it to represent the forgiveness of sins.

Another type of sacrifice was called a thank offering. People showed their love to God or thanked God for a great harvest, victory, or other important event by offering grain, bread, or animals. Part of the offering was burned, and the priests used what was left over.

We no longer offer sacrifices the way Old Testament people did. Jesus' death was a one-time sacrifice for the forgiveness of sin. God now asks us to be living sacrifices for him. Everything we do should show that we are thankful for Jesus' sacrifice on the cross.

SCRIBES

Before Judah was exiled to Babylon, scribes were writers or copiers of the law. Most people did not know how to write, so a scribe's job was very important. Scribes kept the records for the kingdom. Public scribes sat at the city gates and recorded business deals.

After the exile, scribes became teachers of the law. Most people could not read, so scribes read the laws of Moses and taught the people.

By New Testament times, a professional group of scribes had developed. Most of them were Pharisees. They interpreted God's laws and instructed people in the law.

TEMPLE

Solomon's temple was a beautiful building that took over seven years to build.

Solomon patterned the temple after the tabernacle. The temple building had three sections: the porch, the Holy Place, and the Most Holy Place (Holy of Holies). Phoenician craftsmen carved the stone for the walls. They carved the stone at the quarry because no sound of iron tools was supposed to be heard at the temple. The stone walls were covered with cedar wood carved with rosebuds, flowers, palm trees, angels, and chains. The walls, the doors, and everything else inside the temple were covered with gold.

As the priest approached the temple, he entered the porch first. It was 30 feet wide and 15 feet long. Narrow windows lighted the porch. Cedar doors separated the porch and the Holy Place. The Holy Place was 30 feet wide and 60 feet long. The altar of incense, 10 golden lampstands, and 12 tables of showbread were inside the Holy Place.

Once a year a priest entered the innermost room, the Most Holy Place

Model of Solomon's temple

(Holy of Holies). The floor here was higher than those in the Holy Place, and there were no windows. In the Most Holy Place two large carved cherubim (angels) stood on the floor with their wings stretched out over the ark of the covenant.

Rooms built on three sides of the temple were used for storing supplies, for the treasury, and as sleeping rooms for the priests on duty. The rooms were three stories high—each story a little wider than the one immediately lower. Each story was supported with pillars.

The entrance to the temple was on the fourth side, facing east. Two large bronze pillars next to the entrance were carved with chains and pomegranates. These pillars were named Jachin and Boaz.

People gathered in the courtyard around the temple to worship and to offer sacrifices. They never entered the temple itself because it was God's house. The courtyard contained the altar of sacrifice and a huge bronze laver.

The temple was very expensive to build. The Israelites donated many gold items, which were melted and used for the temple walls. Solomon taxed the people to pay the craftsmen and to cover other expenses.

THE CANAANITE ALPHABET

While the Israelites were still in Egypt, some Canaanites invented a new way of writing using an alphabet.

In alphabet writing, symbols stand for a language's sounds, not for words. The Canaanites chose a different symbol for each sound of their language. Each of these symbols represents something. For example, the first picture represents an ox. It stands for the first sound in the Canaanite word for ox. The idea is the same as if we were to use a picture of an apple to stand for the *A* sound.

THE HEBREW ALPHABET

When the Israelites settled in Canaan, they began to use the Canaanite alphabet to write down words of their own language, Hebrew, which was a similar language. This alphabet system was the one used to write down most of the books of the Old Testament.

People have spoken different languages ever since the Tower of Babel.

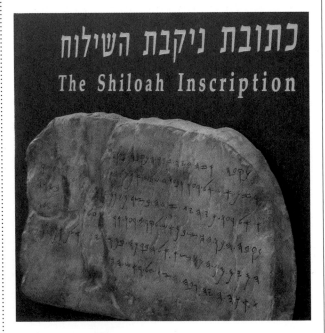

Hebrew writing

When the Old Testament was written, **Hebrew** was the common language of the Israelites. Each letter in the Hebrew alphabet stood for a syllable instead of a sound. There were 22 consonants and no vowels. Hebrew was written from the right to the left, not from the left to the right like English.

When the Israelites went into exile, they lived among people from different countries. The Israelites learned to speak **Aramaic** so that they could communicate with more people. Aramaic was very similar to Hebrew. Jeremiah 10:11, two sections of the Book of Ezra, and much of the Book of Daniel were written in Aramaic.

THE GREEK ALPHABET

During New Testament times the Greeks became very important. Many people learned the **Greek** language. The New Testament was written in Greek so that people in many regions could read it. The Old Testament was translated into Greek during the third or second century B.C. This translation was called the Septuagint.

Greek writing

THE LATIN ALPHABET

The Romans borrowed the Greek alphabet to write down their language. The Romans spread the alphabet throughout Europe, and the people of certain countries began using the Romans letters to write down their own language. These are the letters that led to the English alphabet.

When the Romans became powerful, Latin became the official language. The translation of the Bible into Latin was completed in A.D. 405. This translation was called the Vulgate. The church used the Vulgate until the time of the Reformation.

TRIBUTE

Conquered nations paid tribute to their new leaders. Tribute was like a tax, showing that the people would obey the new government. The new government used the tribute to become more powerful and to keep the conquered nation poor and weak.

Sometimes tribute was paid with money. At other times the people gave livestock, food, horses, expensive clothes, jewels, or property. Some people were forced to be slaves as part of their tribute.

When King Hoshea refused to pay tribute to Assyria, the Assyrians destroyed Israel.

URIM AND THUMMIM

When the people of Israel faced a crisis, they called on the priests to find out what God wanted them to do. The priests determined God's answer by consulting the Urim and Thummim. The high priest carried the Urim and Thummim in a pouch of his ephod.

No one knows for sure what the Urim and Thummim looked like or exactly how they were used because the Bible does not describe these objects. They may have been gems or objects covered in gold or another precious metal. We can compare the use of the Urim and Thummim to the casting of lots or the throwing of dice; the priest may have drawn an object out of the pouch to determine what God wanted the people to do.

Although we do not completely understand how the Israelites used the Urim and Thummim, we do know that they followed God's will as it was revealed through these sacred objects. The remaining tribe of Judah lost the ability to consult the Urim and Thummim when they were exiled to Babylon.

WEAPONS

Israelite soldiers used slings, spears, swords, daggers, clubs, axes, or bows and arrows to defend themselves or to attack other soldiers. Most of the weapons before David's time were made from bronze. The Philistines discovered how to melt iron and make weapons, but the Israelites did not

learn how to do this until later. By the time David was king, his armies had iron weapons, as well as chariots and horses.

The Israelite army was no match for the Assyrian army. The Assyrian army had three sections: foot soldiers, cavalry (soldiers on horseback), and charioteers. They built boats and pontoon bridges from inflated animal skins to fight in swamps and rivers. The Assyrians captured Israel in 722 B.C.

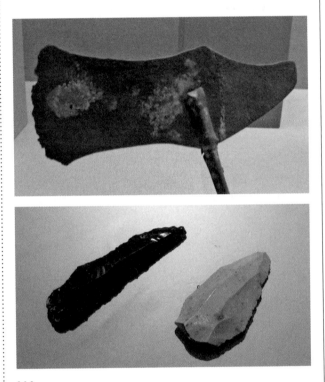

Weapons

WITCHCRAFT

The nations surrounding Israel often practiced witchcraft and magic. Some countries looked for signs in the stars, while others searched for them in animals. The Egyptians saw visions in water and used charms to keep away evil. Magic was used to try to protect kings from evil spirits, as well as to try to talk with other spirits. Some magicians tricked their customers by pretending to talk to spirits.

God told the Israelites never to use witchcraft. The law required that anyone caught using witchcraft was to be put to death. Even so, many Israelites still practiced witchcraft in secret. Even King Saul knew where to find the witch of Endor.

WRITING

Understanding pictographs was hard because everyone drew the pictures differently. So a system of pictures was developed called **hieroglyphics**. Hieroglyphics was a written sign language containing several signs. Joseph may have learned hieroglyphics

Hieroglyphics

when he was working as a slave to the Egyptians.

The Egyptians found that using hieroglyphics was slow, so they developed hieratic, a cursive form of hieroglyphics. People could write faster using hieratics on smooth surfaces, but the pictures were complicated to make and still took a lot of time.

Maps

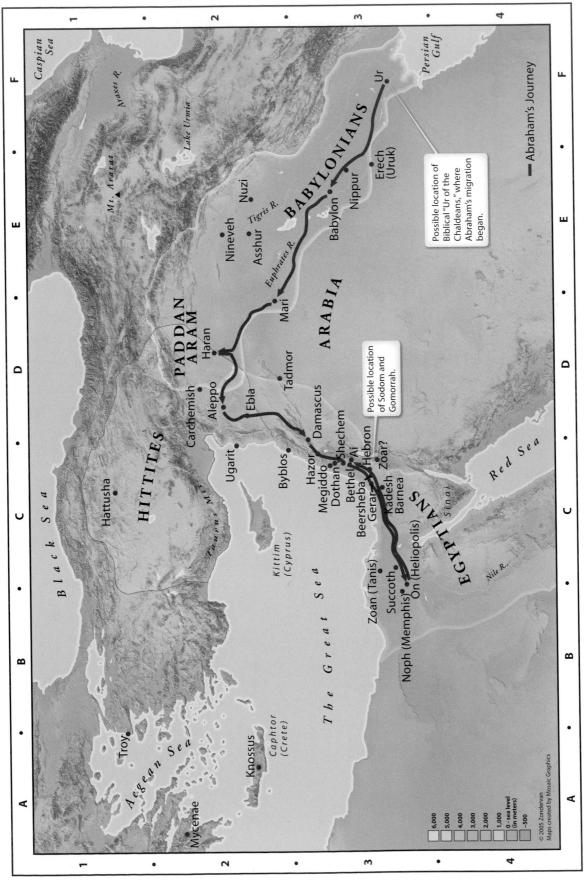

Possible location of Biblical "Ur of the Chaldeans," where Abraham's migration began.

Possible location of Sodom and Gomorrah.

— Abraham's Journey

Caspian Sea

Araxes R.

Lake Urmia

Mt. Ararat

BABYLONIANS

Persian Gulf

Ur

Erech (Uruk)

Nuzi

Nippur

Babylon

Nineveh

Asshur

Tigris R.

Euphrates R.

Mari

ARABIA

PADDAN ARAM

Haran

Tadmor

Carchemish

Aleppo

Ebla

Damascus

HITTITES

Hattusha

Ugarit

Byblos

Hazor

Megiddo

Dothan

Shechem

Ai

Bethel

Hebron

Zoar?

Beersheba

Gerar

Kadesh Barnea

EGYPTIANS

Red Sea

Sinai

Nile R.

Black Sea

Taurus Mts.

Kittim (Cyprus)

The Great Sea

Zoan (Tanis)

Succoth

Noph (Memphis)

On (Heliopolis)

Troy

Aegean Sea

Caphtor (Crete)

Knossus

Mycenae

6,000
5,000
4,000
3,000
2,000
1,000
0 - sea level (in meters)
-500

© 2005 Zondervan
Maps created by Mosaic Graphics

HOLY LAND AND SINAI

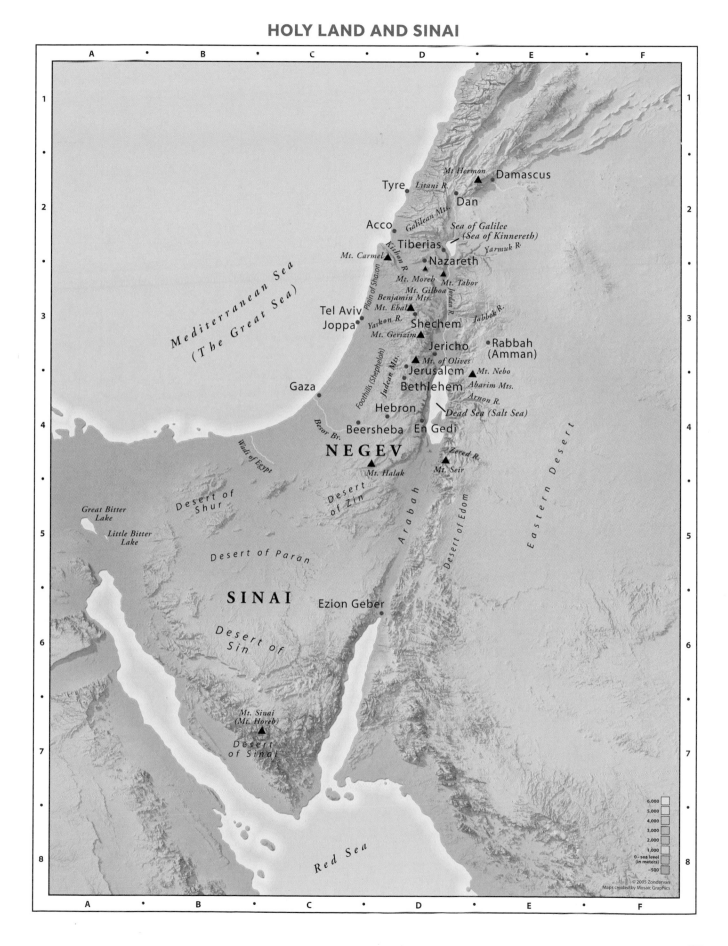

EXODUS AND CONQUEST OF CANAAN

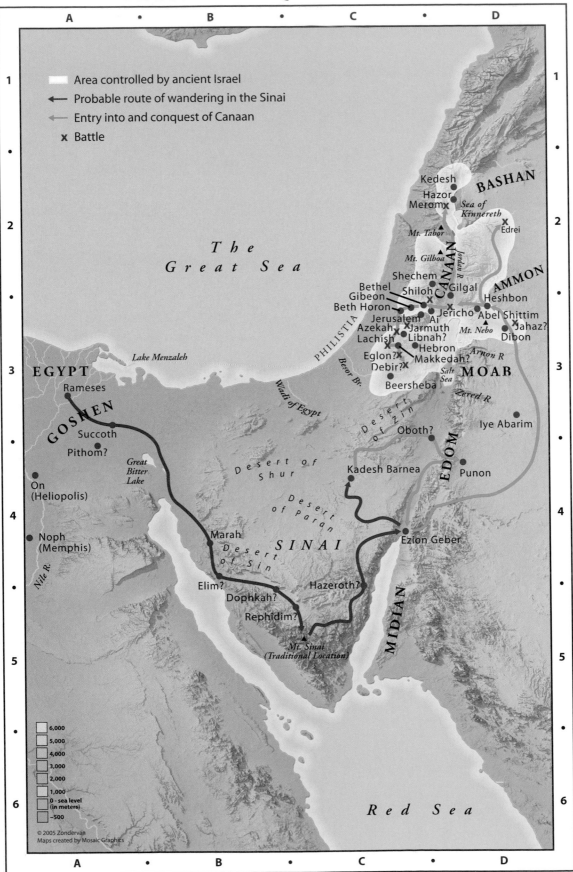

Area controlled by ancient Israel
Probable route of wandering in the Sinai
Entry into and conquest of Canaan
x Battle

Kedesh
BASHAN
Hazor
Merom x
Sea of Kinnereth
Edrei x
Mt. Tabor
Mt. Gilboa
CANAAN
Jordan R.
Shechem
AMMON
Bethel
Shiloh
Gilgal
Heshbon
Gibeon
Beth Horon
Jericho
Abel Shittim
Jerusalem
Ai
Jahaz?
Azekah
Jarmuth
Mt. Nebo
Dibon
Lachish
Libnah?
PHILISTIA
Hebron
Eglon?
Makkedah?
Arnon R.
Besor Br.
Debir?
Salt
MOAB
Beersheba
Sea
Zered R.

The Great Sea

Lake Menzaleh

EGYPT
Rameses
Desert of Zin
GOSHEN
Succoth
Pithom?
Iye Abarim
Wadi of Egypt
Oboth?
EDOM
Great Bitter Lake
Kadesh Barnea
Punon
On (Heliopolis)
Desert of Shur
Noph (Memphis)
Desert of Paran
Nile R.
Marah
SINAI
Ezion Geber
Desert of Sin
Elim?
Hazeroth?
Dophkah?
MIDIAN
Rephidim?
Mt. Sinai (Traditional Location)

6,000
5,000
4,000
3,000
2,000
1,000
0 - sea level (in meters)
-500

Red Sea

© 2005 Zondervan
Maps created by Mosaic Graphics

A   B   C   D

LAND OF THE TWELVE TRIBES

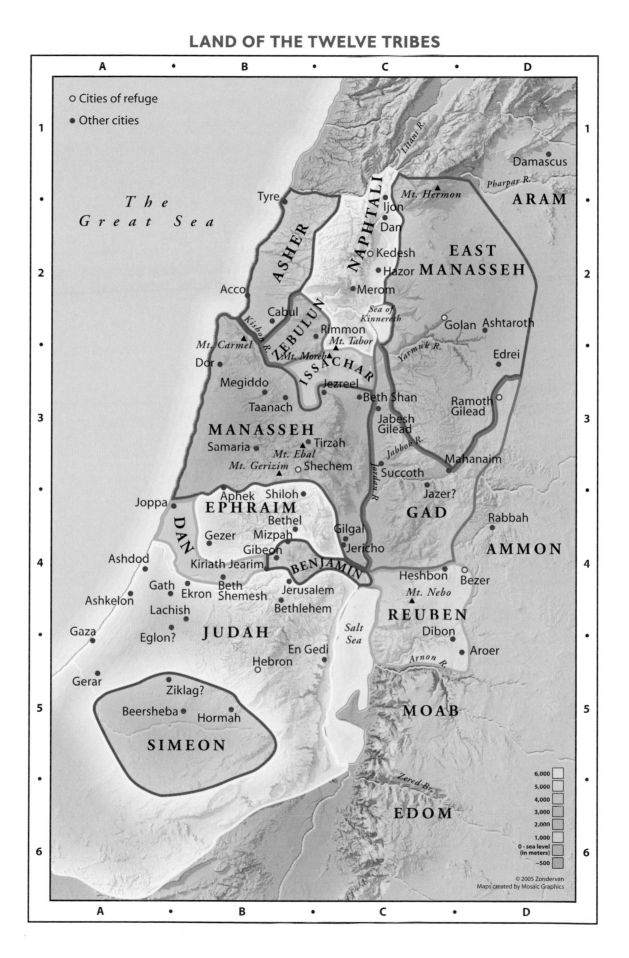

Cities of refuge
Other cities

The Great Sea

Tyre

ASHER

NAPHTALI

Litani R.

Damascus

Pharpar R.

ARAM

Mt. Hermon

Ijon

Dan

EAST
MANASSEH

Kedesh

Hazor

Acco

Merom

Sea of
Kinnereth

Golan

Ashtaroth

Cabul

ZEBULUN

Rimmon

Kishon R.

Mt. Carmel

Mt. Tabor

Mt. Moreh

ISSACHAR

Yarmuk R.

Edrei

Dor

Megiddo

Jezreel

Beth Shan

Ramoth
Gilead

Taanach

Jabesh
Gilead

MANASSEH

Jabbok R.

Samaria

Tirzah

Mt. Ebal

Mahanaim

Mt. Gerizim

Shechem

Jordan R.

Succoth

Aphek

Shiloh

Jazer?

Joppa

EPHRAIM

Bethel

DAN

Gezer

Mizpah

Gilgal

GAD

Rabbah

Gibeon

Jericho

Ashdod

Kiriath Jearim

BENJAMIN

AMMON

Gath

Beth
Shemesh

Jerusalem

Heshbon

Bezer

Ashkelon

Ekron

Bethlehem

Mt. Nebo

Lachish

Gaza

Eglon?

JUDAH

En Gedi

Salt
Sea

REUBEN

Dibon

Hebron

Aroer

Gerar

Arnon R.

Ziklag?

MOAB

Beersheba

Hormah

SIMEON

Zered Br.

EDOM

6,000
5,000
4,000
3,000
2,000
1,000
0 - sea level
(in meters)
-500

© 2005 Zondervan
Maps created by Mosaic Graphics

KINGDOMS OF DAVID AND SOLOMON

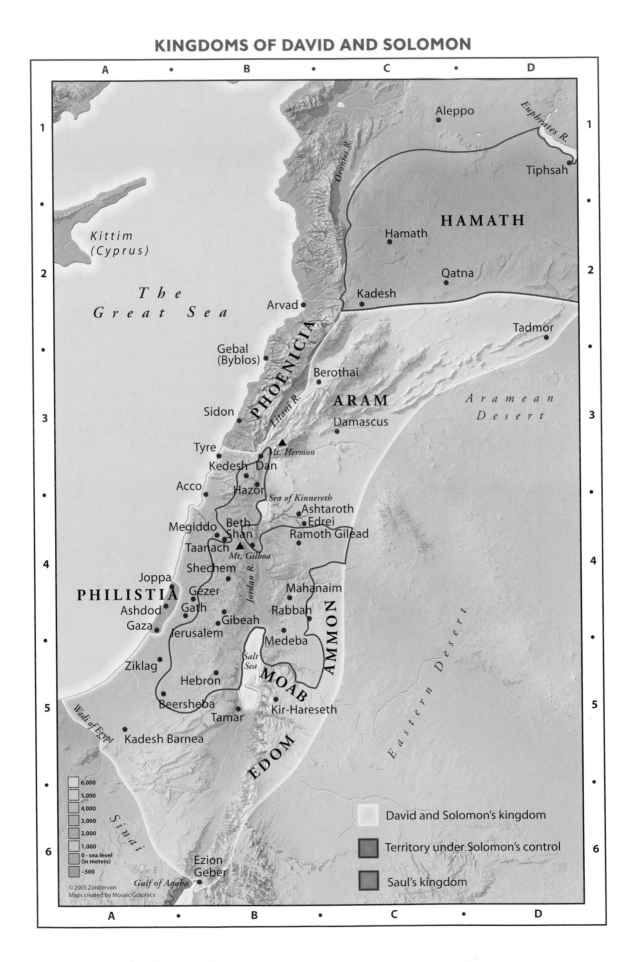

Aleppo

Euphrates R.

Tiphsah

HAMATH

Hamath

Qatna

Kadesh

Tadmor

The Great Sea

Kittim (Cyprus)

Arvad

Aramean Desert

Gebal (Byblos)

Berothai

ARAM

PHOENICIA

Sidon

Damascus

Litani R.

Tyre

Mt. Hermon

Kedesh Dan

Acco

Hazor

Sea of Kinnereth

Ashtaroth

Megiddo

Beth Shan

Edrei

Taanach

Ramoth Gilead

Mt. Gilboa

Shechem

Jordan R.

Joppa

Mahanaim

PHILISTIA

Gezer

Ashdod

Gath

Rabbah

AMMON

Gaza

Gibeah

Jerusalem

Medeba

Ziklag

Salt Sea

Hebron

MOAB

Beersheba

Kir-Hareseth

Tamar

Eastern Desert

Wadi of Egypt

Kadesh Barnea

EDOM

Sinai

6,000
5,000
4,000
3,000
2,000
1,000
0 - sea level (in meters)
−500

Ezion Geber

Gulf of Aqaba

© 2005 Zondervan
Maps created by Mosaic Graphics

David and Solomon's kingdom

Territory under Solomon's control

Saul's kingdom

KINGDOMS OF ISRAEL AND JUDAH

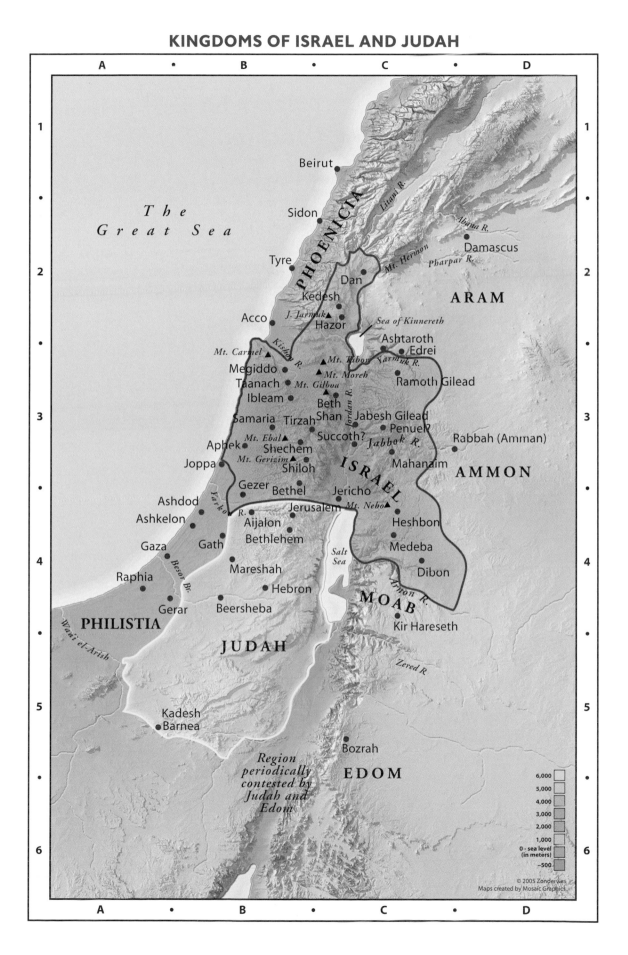

The Great Sea

Beirut

Sidon

PHOENICIA

Litani R.

Abana R.

Damascus

Tyre

Dan

Mt. Hermon

Pharpar R.

ARAM

Kedesh

Acco

J. Jarmuk ▲

Hazor

Sea of Kinnereth

Ashtaroth

Edrei

Mt. Carmel ▲

Kishon R.

▲ Mt. Tabor

Yarmuk R.

Megiddo

▲ Mt. Moreh

Ramoth Gilead

Taanach

Mt. Gilboa ▲

Ibleam

Beth

Jordan R.

Jabesh Gilead

Samaria

Tirzah

Shan

Penuel?

Aphek

Mt. Ebal ▲

Succoth?

Jabbok R.

Rabbah (Amman)

Shechem

Joppa

Mt. Gerizim ▲

Shiloh

ISRAEL

Mahanaim

AMMON

Gezer

Bethel

Jericho

Ashdod

Yarkon R.

Jerusalem

Mt. Nebo ▲

Heshbon

Ashkelon

Aijalon

Bethlehem

Medeba

Gaza

Gath

Salt
Sea

Dibon

Raphia

Besor Br.

Mareshah

Hebron

Arnon R.

Gerar

Beersheba

MOAB

PHILISTIA

Kir Hareseth

Wadi el-Arish

JUDAH

Zered R.

Kadesh
Barnea

Bozrah

Region
periodically
contested by
Judah and
Edom

EDOM

6,000
5,000
4,000
3,000
2,000
1,000
0 - sea level
(in meters)
−500

© 2005 Zondervan
Maps created by Mosaic Graphics

PROPHETS IN ISRAEL AND JUDAH

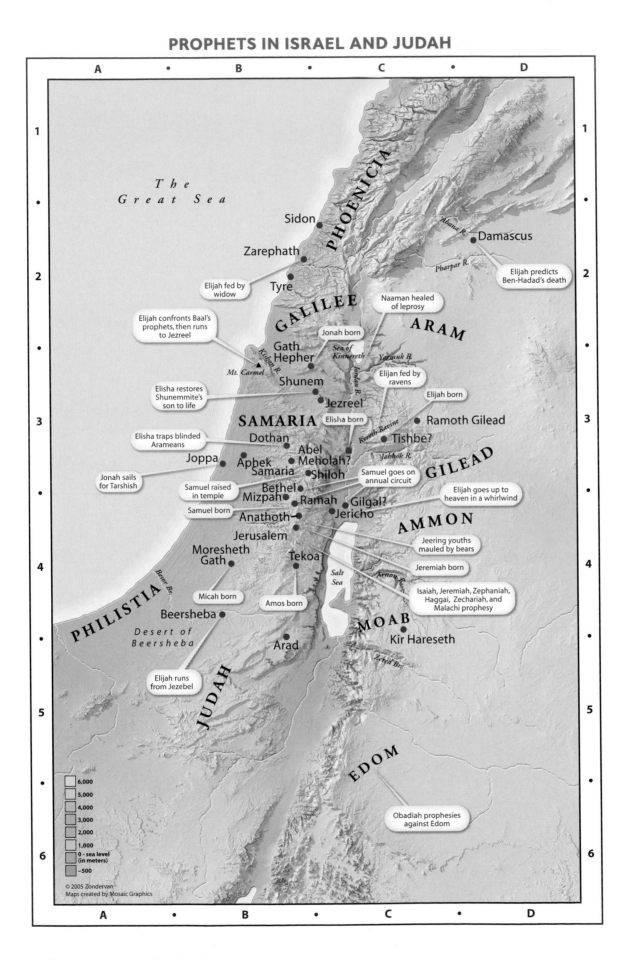

The Great Sea

Sidon

Abana R.

Damascus

Zarephath

PHOENICIA

Elijah predicts
Ben-Hadad's death

Pharpar R.

Tyre

Elijah fed by
widow

Naaman healed
of leprosy

ARAM

GALILEE

Jonah born

Elijah confronts Baal's
prophets, then runs
to Jezreel

Gath
Hepher

Sea of
Kinnereth

Yarmuk R.

Kishon R.

Mt. Carmel

Shunem

Jordan R.

Elijah fed by
ravens

Elisha restores
Shunemmite's
son to life

Jezreel

Elijah born

Elisha born

Ramoth Gilead

SAMARIA

Kereth Ravine

Tishbe?

Elisha traps blinded
Arameans

Dothan

Jabbok R.

Joppa

Abel
Meholah?

Aphek

GILEAD

Samaria

Shiloh

Jonah sails
for Tarshish

Samuel goes on
annual circuit

Elijah goes up to
heaven in a whirlwind

Bethel

Samuel raised
in temple

Mizpah

Ramah

Gilgal?

AMMON

Samuel born

Jericho

Anathoth

Jeering youths
mauled by bears

Jerusalem

Moresheth
Gath

Tekoa

Salt
Sea

Arnon R.

Jeremiah born

Micah born

Amos born

Isaiah, Jeremiah, Zephaniah,
Haggai, Zechariah, and
Malachi prophesy

PHILISTIA

Beersheba

Desert of
Beersheba

MOAB

Kir Hareseth

Arad

Zered Br.

Elijah runs
from Jezebel

JUDAH

EDOM

6,000
5,000
4,000
3,000
2,000
1,000
0 - sea level
(in meters)
-500

Obadiah prophesies
against Edom

© 2005 Zondervan
Maps created by Mosaic Graphics

ASSYRIAN AND BABYLONIAN EMPIRES

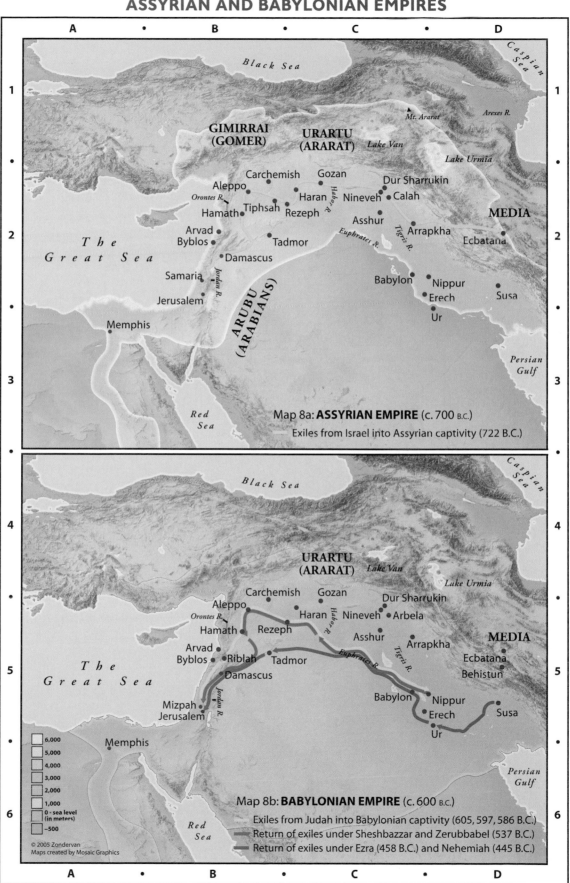

Map 8a: **ASSYRIAN EMPIRE** (c. 700 B.C.)

Exiles from Israel into Assyrian captivity (722 B.C.)

Map 8b: **BABYLONIAN EMPIRE** (c. 600 B.C.)

Exiles from Judah into Babylonian captivity (605, 597, 586 B.C.)
Return of exiles under Sheshbazzar and Zerubbabel (537 B.C.)
Return of exiles under Ezra (458 B.C.) and Nehemiah (445 B.C.)

© 2005 Zondervan
Maps created by Mosaic Graphics

HOLY LAND IN THE TIME OF JESUS

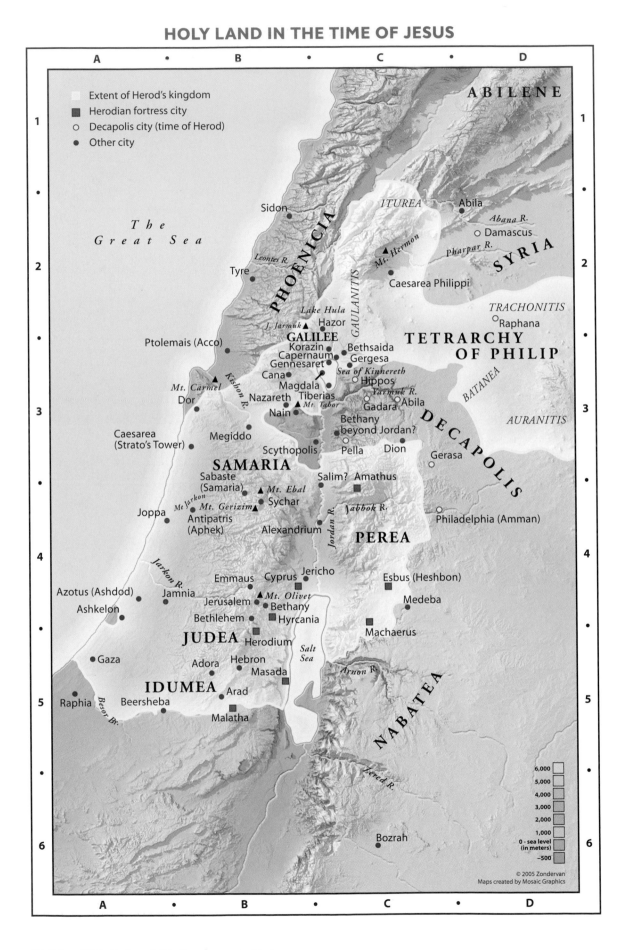

Extent of Herod's kingdom
Herodian fortress city
Decapolis city (time of Herod)
Other city

ABILENE

The Great Sea

ITUREA

Abila

Abana R.

Sidon

○ Damascus

Pharpar R.

SYRIA

Leontes R.

PHOENICIA

▲ *Mt. Hermon*

Tyre

Caesarea Philippi

Lake Hula

TRACHONITIS

○ Raphana

J. Jarmuk ▲ Hazor

GAULANITIS

Ptolemais (Acco)

GALILEE
Korazin

Bethsaida

TETRARCHY
OF PHILIP

Capernaum

Gergesa

Gennesaret

Sea of Kinnereth

BATANEA

Cana

○ Hippos

▲ *Mt. Carmel*

Kishon R.

Magdala

Yarmuk R.

Dor

Nazareth

Tiberias

Gadara ● Abila

AURANITIS

▲ *Mt. Tabor*

Nain

Bethany
beyond Jordan?

DECAPOLIS

Caesarea
(Strato's Tower)

Megiddo

Pella

Dion

○ Gerasa

Scythopolis

SAMARIA

Sabaste
(Samaria)

▲ *Mt. Ebal*

Salim? ■ Amathus

Me Jarkon

▲ *Mt. Gerizim* ▲ Sychar

Jabbok R.

Joppa

Jordan R.

○ Philadelphia (Amman)

Antipatris
(Aphek)

Alexandrium

PEREA

Jarkon R.

Emmaus

Cyprus

Jericho

Azotus (Ashdod)

Jamnia

▲ *Mt. Olivet*

Esbus (Heshbon) ■

Ashkelon

Jerusalem

Bethany

Medeba

Bethlehem

■ Hyrcania

● Gaza

JUDEA

Herodium ■

*Salt
Sea*

■ Machaerus

Adora

Hebron

Arnon R.

Masada ■

Raphia

Besor Br.

Beersheba

IDUMEA

Arad

NABATEA

Malatha ■

Zered R.

6,000
5,000
4,000
3,000
2,000
1,000
0 - sea level
(in meters)
−500

Bozrah

© 2005 Zondervan
Maps created by Mosaic Graphics

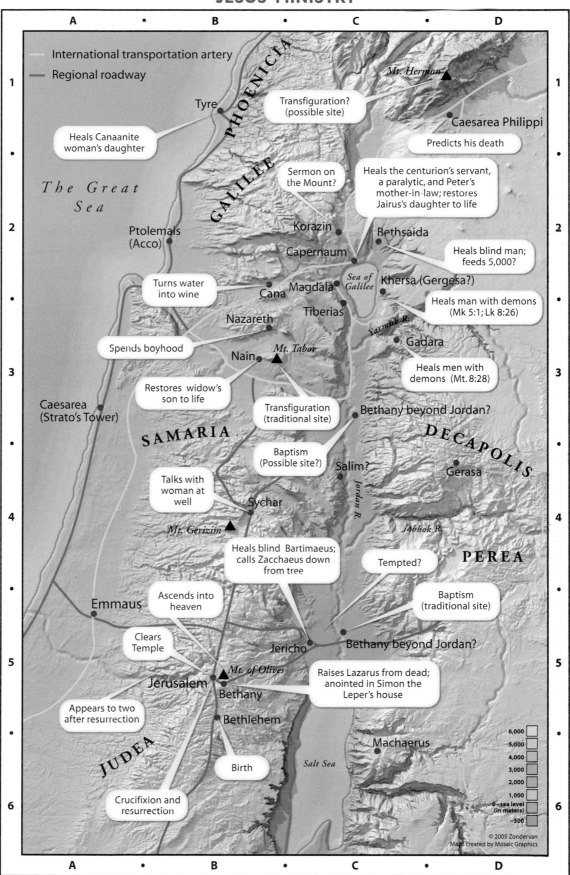

A • B • C • D

International transportation artery
Regional roadway

PHOENICIA

Mt. Hermon ▲

Tyre

Caesarea Philippi

Transfiguration?
(possible site)

Heals Canaanite
woman's daughter

Predicts his death

GALILEE

Sermon on
the Mount?

Heals the centurion's servant,
a paralytic, and Peter's
mother-in-law; restores
Jairus's daughter to life

*The Great
Sea*

Ptolemais
(Acco)

Korazin

Bethsaida

Capernaum

Heals blind man;
feeds 5,000?

Turns water
into wine

Cana

Magdala

*Sea of
Galilee*

Khersa (Gergesa?)

Nazareth

Tiberias

Yarmuk R.

Heals man with demons
(Mk 5:1; Lk 8:26)

Spends boyhood

Nain

Mt. Tabor ▲

Gadara

Heals men with
demons (Mt. 8:28)

Caesarea
(Strato's Tower)

Restores widow's
son to life

Transfiguration
(traditional site)

Bethany beyond Jordan?

DECAPOLIS

SAMARIA

Baptism
(Possible site?)

Salim?

Jordan R.

Gerasa

Talks with
woman at
well

Sychar

Jabbok R.

Mt. Gerizim ▲

PEREA

Heals blind Bartimaeus;
calls Zacchaeus down
from tree

Tempted?

Emmaus

Ascends into
heaven

Baptism
(traditional site)

Clears
Temple

Jericho

Bethany beyond Jordan?

Mt. of Olives ▲

Jerusalem

Raises Lazarus from dead;
anointed in Simon the
Leper's house

Bethany

Appears to two
after resurrection

Bethlehem

Machaerus

JUDEA

Salt Sea

Birth

6,000
5,000
4,000
3,000
2,000
1,000
0 - sea level
(in meters)
-500

Crucifixion and
resurrection

© 2005 Zondervan
Maps created by Mosaic Graphics

ROMAN EMPIRE

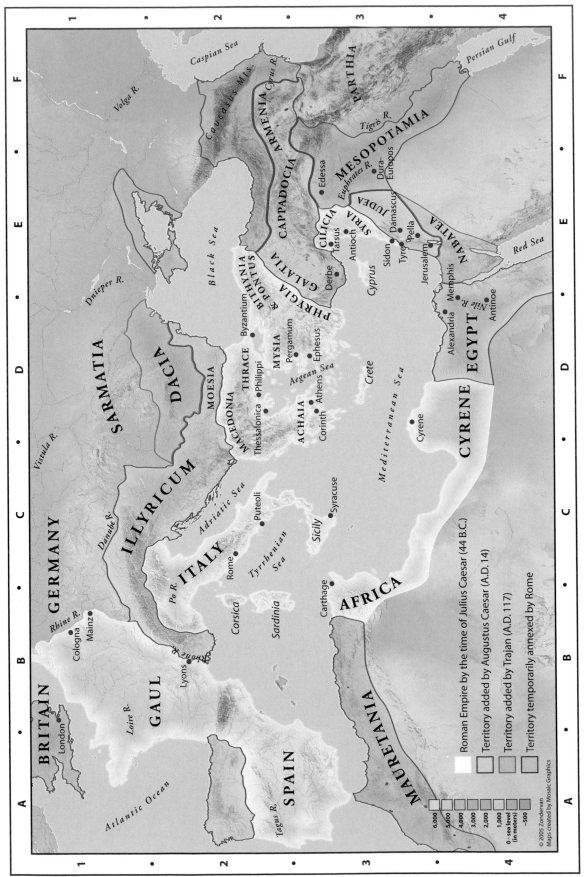

Roman Empire by the time of Julius Caesar (44 B.C.)

Territory added by Augustus Caesar (A.D.14)

Territory added by Trajan (A.D. 117)

Territory temporarily annexed by Rome

sea level (in meters)
6,000
5,000
4,000
3,000
2,000
1,000
0
−500

© 2005 Zondervan
Maps created by Mosaic Graphics

BRITAIN
London

GERMANY
Cologne
Mainz
Rhine R.

GAUL
Lyons
Loire R.
Rhone R.

SPAIN
Tagus R.

MAURETANIA

AFRICA
Carthage

ITALY
Rome
Po R.
Corsica
Sardinia
Sicily
Puteoli
Syracuse

Atlantic Ocean

SARMATIA
Vistula R.
Dnieper R.

DACIA
Danube R.

ILLYRICUM
Adriatic Sea

MOESIA

MACEDONIA
Thessalonica

THRACE
Byzantium
Philippi

ACHAIA
Corinth
Athens

Aegean Sea
Athens Sea

MYSIA
Pergamum
Ephesus

Tyrrhenian Sea

Mediterranean Sea

Black Sea

Caspian Sea

Volga R.

Caucasus Mts.

ARMENIA
Cyrus R.

PARTHIA

Persian Gulf

Tigris R.

MESOPOTAMIA
Dura-Europos

CAPPADOCIA
Edessa
Euphrates R.

GALATIA

PHRYGIA
Derbe

BITHYNIA & PONTUS

CILICIA
Tarsus

SYRIA
Antioch

JUDEA
Damascus
Sidon
Tyre
Pella
Jerusalem

NABATEA

Cyprus

Crete

Red Sea

CYRENE
Cyrene

EGYPT
Alexandria
Memphis
Antinoe
Nile R.

EARLY TRAVELS OF THE APOSTLES

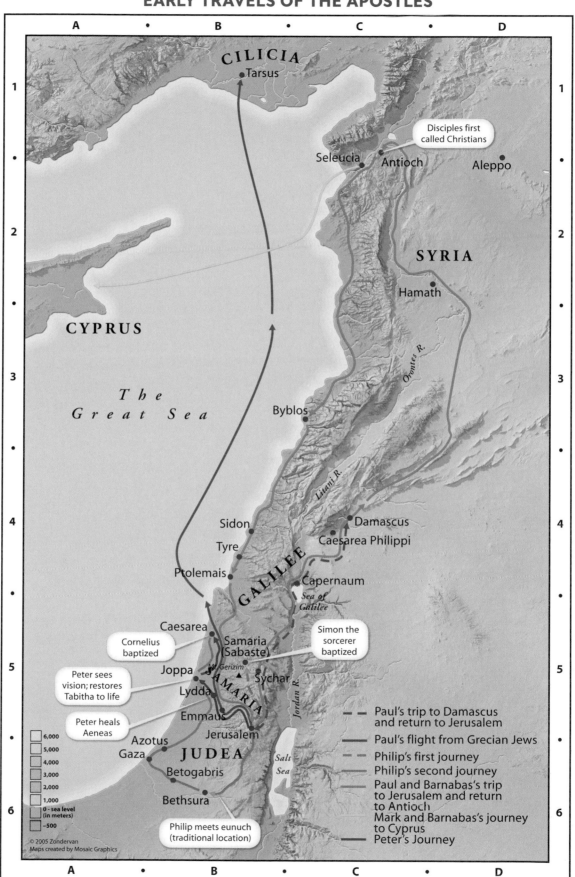

CILICIA
Tarsus

Disciples first
called Christians

Seleucia · Antioch · Aleppo

SYRIA

Hamath

Orontes R.

CYPRUS

*The
Great Sea*

Byblos

Litani R.

Sidon · Damascus
Tyre · Caesarea Philippi

Ptolemais

GALILEE

Capernaum

*Sea of
Galilee*

Caesarea

Samaria
(Sabaste)

Simon the
sorcerer
baptized

Cornelius
baptized

Joppa

Mt. Gerizim · Sychar

Peter sees
vision; restores
Tabitha to life

Lydda

SAMARIA

Jordan R.

Emmaus

Peter heals
Aeneas

Jerusalem

Azotus
Gaza

JUDEA

*Salt
Sea*

Betogabris

Bethsura

Philip meets eunuch
(traditional location)

6,000
5,000
4,000
3,000
2,000
1,000
0 - sea level
(in meters)
−500

© 2005 Zondervan
Maps created by Mosaic Graphics

- - - Paul's trip to Damascus
and return to Jerusalem

——— Paul's flight from Grecian Jews

- - - Philip's first journey

——— Philip's second journey

——— Paul and Barnabas's trip
to Jerusalem and return
to Antioch

Mark and Barnabas's journey
to Cyprus

——— Peter's Journey

PAULS' MISSIONARY JOURNEYS

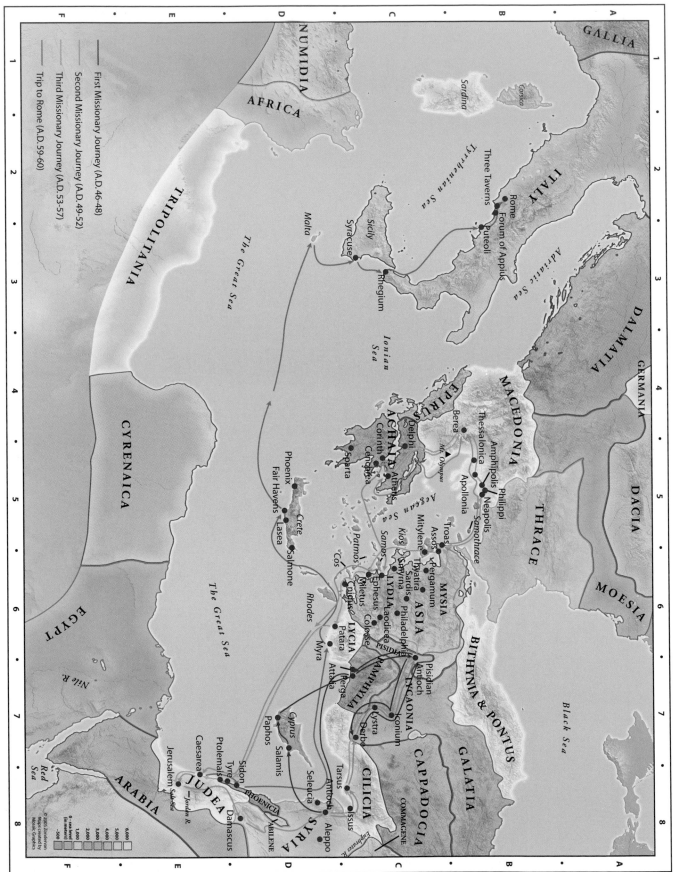

Timeline

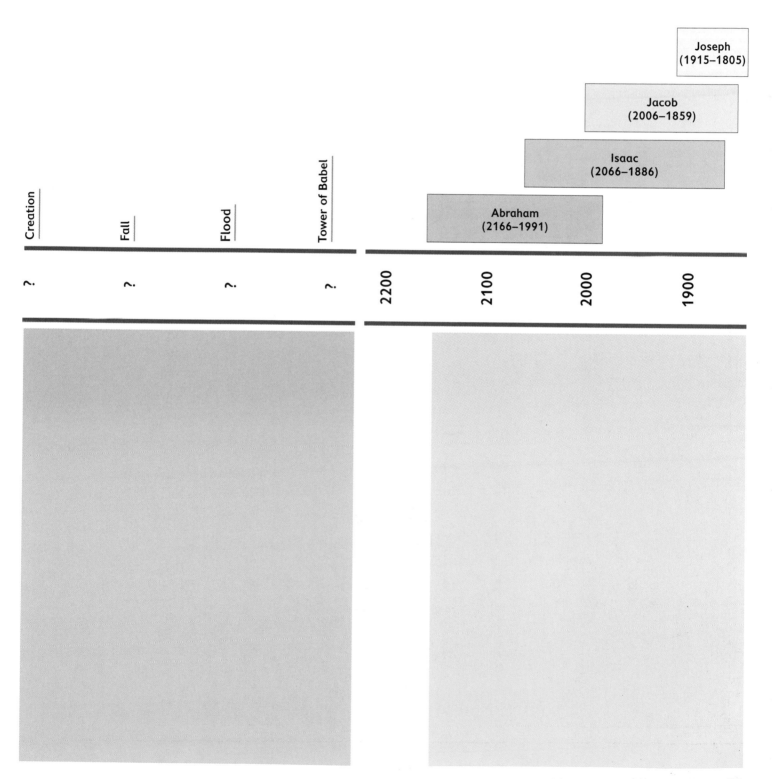

Creation

Fall

Flood

Tower of Babel

? ? ? ?

2200 2100 2000 1900

Joseph
(1915–1805)

Jacob
(2006–1859)

Isaac
(2066–1886)

Abraham
(2166–1991)

Joseph
(1915–1805)

The Exodus

Settling the Promised Land

1900

1800

1700

1600

1500

1400

1300

1200

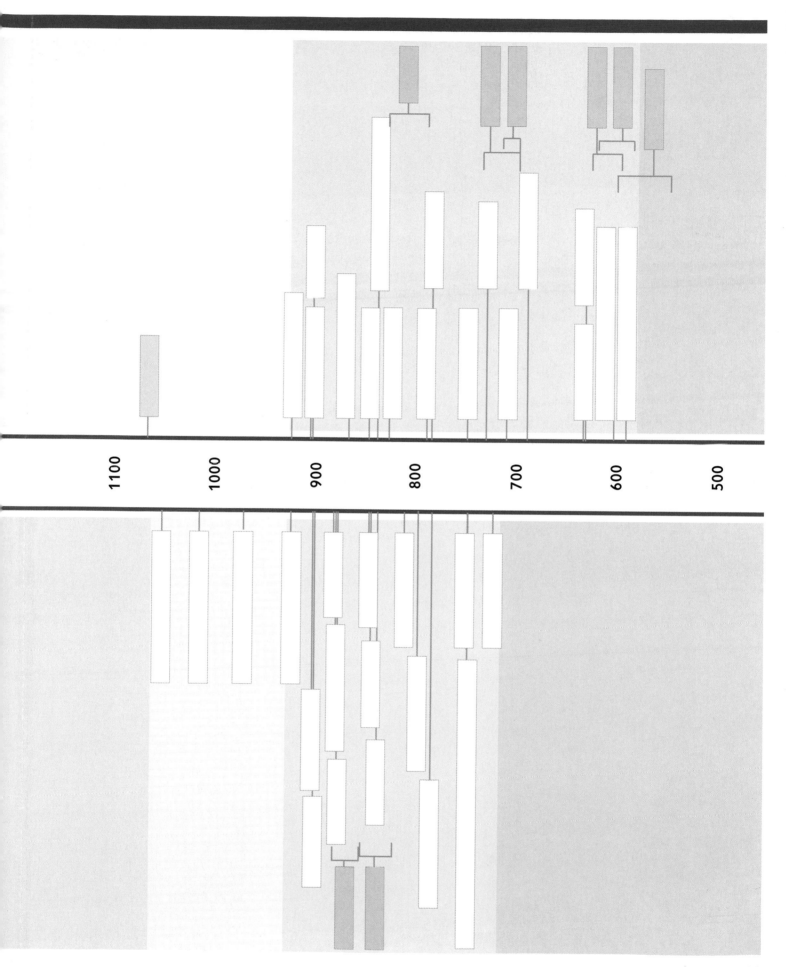

1100

1000

900

800

700

600

500

B.C. | A.D.

Between the Testaments

500   400   300   200   100   100